Table of Contents

Sections: Day:

(Answer Key in Back)

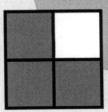

Name: _____

Score:

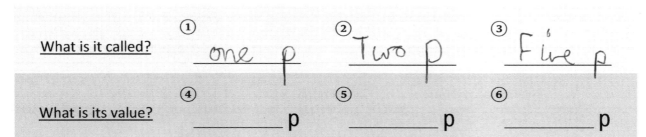

1p   2p   5p

① What is it called? __one p__
② __Two p__
③ __Five p__

④ What is its value? _____ p
⑤ _____ p
⑥ _____ p

Write the value of each group of coins.

2p 5p
⑦ ___7___ p

5p 5p 5p 5p
⑧ ___20___ p

1p 1p 5p
⑨ ___7___ p

5p 5p 2p 2p
⑩ ___14___ p

Add the following values. (Don't forget to include the money symbol after your answer.)

⑪
```
  12p
+  8p
 20 P
```

⑫
```
  26p
+ 10p
  36p
```

⑬
```
   5p
+ 53p
  58P
```

⑭
```
  32p
+ 19p
  51 P
```

⑮
```
  16p
+ 76p
  92P
```

⑯
```
  22p
+ 37p
```

⑰
```
   4p
+ 11p
```

⑱
```
  38p
+ 45p
  83P
```

⑲
```
  62p
+  9p
  71P
```

⑳
```
  80p
+ 10p
  90 P
```

Day 2
1p, 2p, & 5p coins

Name: DYLAN

Score:

Write the value of each group of coins.

① ___8___ p

② ___10___ p

③ ___19___ p

④ ___13___ p

Write the value of each group of coins.

⑤ Two 5p coins
Five 2p coins
Three 1p coins   ___23___ p

⑥ One 5p coins
Two 2p coins
Six 1p coins   ___15___ p

⑦ Six 5p coins
Three 2p coins
One 1p coins   ___37___ p

⑧ Four 5p coins
One 2p coins
Nine 1p coins   ___31___ p

⑨ Five 5p coins
Seven 1p coins   ___32___ p

⑩ Three 5p coins ^15
12 Six 2p coins
4 Four 1p coins   ___31___ p

⑪ Eight 5p coins
Four 2p coins
Two 1p coins   ___50___ p

⑫ Two 5p coins ^10
4 Two 2p coins
5 Five 1p coins   ___19___ p

Name: Dylan

Score:

Write the value for each group of coins.

① _____10_____ p ✓

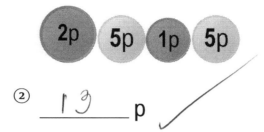

② _____13_____ p ✓

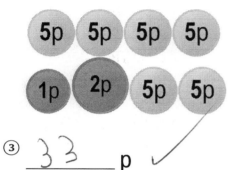

③ __33__ p ✓

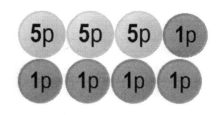

④ _____20_____ p ✓

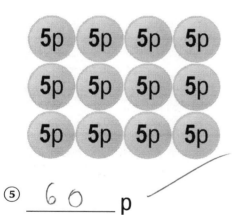

⑤ __6 0__ p

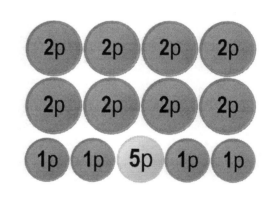

⑥ __2 5__ p ✓

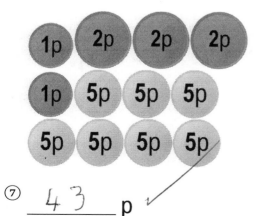

⑦ __4 3__ p

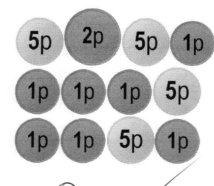

⑧ __2 9__ p ✓

Name: _____

Score:

10p   **20p**   **50p**

What is it called?	① Ten p ~~Tex~~	② Twenty p	③ Fisty p ~~five~~
What is its value?	④ 10 p	⑤ 20 p	⑥ 50 p

Write the value for each group of coins.

20p 10p 50p 5p 5p

⑦ 90 p ✓

10p 5p 5p 20p

⑧ 40 p ✓

10p 50p 2p 2p
1p 20p

⑨ 86 p ✓

20p 2p 5p
10p 10p 10p 10p

⑩ 67 p ✓

10p 5p 5p 20p
20p 1p 10p 1p

⑪ 72 p ✓

20p 1p 20p
10p 1p 20p 2p

⑫ 74 p ✓

Name: _____

Score:

Write the value for each group of coins.

20p 20p 5p 20p

① _6 5_____ p

20p 5p 5p 20p

② _50_____ p

5p 5p 20p 10p
1p 1p 5p 10p

③ _57_____ p

20p 50p 20p 1p
1p 1p 1p 1p

④ _95_____ p

5p 5p 5p 1p
20p 1p 20p 10p
1p 10p 1p 1p

⑤ _7 5_____ p

20p 20p 2p 2p
10p 1p 20p 1p
1p 1p 10p 1p

⑥ _89_____ p

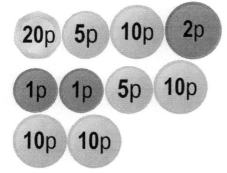

⑦ _6 9_____ p

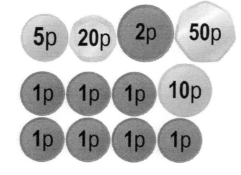

⑧ _94_____ p

Write the value for each group of coins.

20p **1p** **10p** **5p**

① ___36___ p

1p **1p** **20p** **20p** **5p**

② ___X 47___ p

20p **2p** **20p** **20p** *6 2*
1p **1p** **1p** **1p** **1p** *5*

③ ___67___ p

40 60 80 90

20p **1p** **20p** **10p**
10p **20p** **10p** **1p**

④ ___92___ p

Write the value of each group of coins.

⑤
2 20p coins *6 6*
2 10p coin
1 5p coin ___36___ p
1 1p coins

⑥ *6 8*
3 20p coins
₁₅3 5p coins ___83___ p
₈8 1p coins

⑦ *5 0*
1 50p coins
₃₀3 10p coins ___107___ p
₁ ₒ2 5p coins
₁7₁7 1p coins

⑧ *40*
2 20p coins
₂₅5 5p coins ___65___ p

⑨
₆ₒ3 20p coins
₁ₒ1 10p coin ___74___ p
4 2 2p coins

⑩ *2 6*
1 20p coins
₂ ₒ2 10p coins ___61___ p
₂₁21 1p coins

⑪ *4 0*
2 20p coins
₁ₒ1 10p coin ___69___ p
₁5 3 5p coins
4 4 1p coins

⑫ *5 0*
1 50p coins
₁ ₒ1 10p coin ___79___ p
5 1 5p coin
8 4 2p coin
6 6 1p coin

Name: _____

Score:

Solve the following word problems.

① Ben has 34p and Sonia has 50p. How much money do they have together?

② Angela buys a pencil for 35p and a notebook for 49p at the store. How much did she spend?

③ Jason had a 20p coin and three 5p coins, then he found four 10p coins. How much money does Jason have now?

④ Rebecca was given a 50p coin for washing dishes and two 20p coins for weeding the garden. How much money did she earn?

⑤ Tyler had six 5p coins and eight 1p coins, then his grandmother gave him a 50p for his birthday. How much money does Tyler have now?

⑥ Rachel wants to buy a bracelet for herself and a bracelet for her friend. Each bracelet costs 39p. How much money will Rachel need?

⑦ Grace has 72p. Her brother has 16p. How much do they have together?

⑧ Ava has a lemonade stand. She earned three 5p coins and seven 2p coins in the morning. In the afternoon she earned two 5p coins and eight 1p coins. How much money did she make all together?

Day 8

Name: _____

Score:

Subtract the following values. (Don't forget to include the money symbol.)

① 76p − 54p

② 31p −10p

③ 42p −13p

④ 95p −29p

⑤ 58p −55p

⑥ 81p − 7p

⑦ 60p −45p

⑧ 22p −12p

⑨ 38p − 6p

⑩ 75p −28p

Solve the following word problems.

⑪ Evan had three 20p coins and two 10p coins, then he bought a toy car for 55p. How much money did he have left after the purchase?

⑫ Luke has 72p. His sister has two 20p and four 5p coins. How much more money does Luke have than his sister?

⑬ Ruby had four 10p and six 5p coins, then she bought a pack of gum for 35p. How much money did Ruby have after the purchase?

⑭ Darcie had 50p, then a 10p coin and eight 1p coins fell from a hole in her pocket and she lost them. How much money does she have left?

⑮ Mike wants to buy a hotdog. It costs 95p. He only has a 50p and two 2p. How much more money does he need to buy the hotdog?

© Libro Studio LLC 2020

Name: _____

Score:

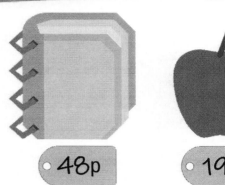   

48p   19p   12p   5p

Use the images above to solve each problem. If a purchase is made round the total to the nearest 5¢

① Holly has 26p. How much money would she have left after buying an apple?

② William wants to buy two notebooks. How much money will that cost?

③ Lola gives the clerk four 20p coins when buying a notebook and an apple. How much change should the clerk give Lola back?

④ Rebecca has a 20p, a 10p, and seven 1p coins. How many crayons can she buy?

⑤ Archie has two 20p and seven 5p coins. How much money would he have left if he buys a pencil and an apple?

⑥ Logan had a 20p, four 10p, three 5p, and thirteen 1p before buying 2 pencils. How much money does he have now?

Name: _____

Score:

Counting by 20 Pence

<u>What is the value?</u>

① 20p

£ 0.20

② 20p 20p

£ _____

③ 20p 20p 20p

£ _____

④ 20p 20p 20p 20p

£ _____

⑤ 20p 20p 20p 20p 20p

£ _____

⑥ 20p 20p 20p 20p 20p 20p

£ _____

⑦ 20p 20p 20p 20p 20p 20p 20p

£ _____

⑧ 20p 20p 20p 20p 20p 20p 20p 20p

£ _____

⑨ 20p 20p 20p 20p 20p 20p 20p 20p 20p

£ _____

⑩ 20p 20p 20p 20p 20p 20p 20p 20p 20p 20p

£ _____

Write the value of each group of coins.

⑪
20p 20p 20p
20p 20p 20p
20p 20p 20p
20p 20p
20p 20p

£ _____

⑫
20p 20p 20p 20p
20p 20p 20p 20p
20p 20p 20p
20p 20p 20p 20p
20p 20p 20p 20p

£ _____

⑬
20p 20p 20p 20p 20p
20p 20p 20p 20p 20p
20p 20p 20p 20p 20p
20p 20p 20p 20p 20p
20p 20p 20p 20p 20p

£ _____

⑭
20p 20p 20p 20p 20p
20p 20p 20p 20p
20p 20p 20p 20p
20p 20p 20p 20p
20p 20p 20p 20p

£ _____

Name: _____

Score:

Add the following values. (Don't forget to include the pound symbol.)

① £1.22
+£0.65

② £1.04
+£3.18

③ £7.92
+£0.99

④ £5.81
+£6.59

⑤ £0.70
+£8.25

Write the value of each group of coins.

20p 20p 20p 20p 20p 1p
5p 5p 1p 5p

20p 10p 20p 20p 20p
5p 10p 10p 10p

⑥ £_____

⑦ £_____

20p 20p 20p 20p 20p 20p
20p 5p 1p 1p

20p 20p 20p 20p 20p
20p 20p 5p

⑧ £_____

⑨ £_____

Write the value of each group of coins.

⑩ 6 20p coins
5 10p coins
14 1p coins
£_____

⑪ 11 20p coins
1 10p coins
4 5p coins
£_____

⑫ 15 20p coins
4 10p coins
5 1p coins
£_____

⑬ 8 20p coins
3 10p coins
2 5p coins
9 1p coins
£_____

⑭ 12 20p coins
1 10p coins
1 5p coin
24 1p coins
£_____

⑮ 10 20p coins
8 10p coins
2 5p coins
7 1p coins
£_____

© Libro Studio LLC 2020

Day 12

Name: _____

Score:

Make each problem equivalent.

① 5 (1p) = ___ (5p)

② 4 (5p) = ___ (10p)

③ 1 (50p) = ___ (1p)

④ 2 (5p) = ___ (1p)

⑤ 4 (5p) = ___ (20p)

⑥ 2 (20p) = ___ (10p)

⑦ 6 (10p) = ___ (5p)

⑧ 5 (10p) = ___ (1p)

⑨ 20 (1p) = ___ (2p)

⑩ 2 (20p) = ___ (5p)

⑪ 7 (5p) = ___ (1p)

⑫ 2 (50p) = ___ (10p)

⑬ 2 (20p) = ___ (1p)

⑭ 4 (10p) = ___ (5p)

⑮ 90 (1p) = ___ (10p)

⑯ 3 (20p) = ___ (5p)

Name: _____

Score:

Subtract the following values. (Don't forget to include the pound symbol.)

① £6.89
−£3.50

② £8.29
−£0.75

③ £5.98
−£5.27

④ £9.70
−£1.64

⑤ £0.81
−£0.25

Solve the following word problems.

⑥ Phoebe had £4.25, then she earned £2.75 for babysitting. How much money does she have now?

⑦ Theo has £2.44 and Clair has £5.27. How much is that together?

⑧ The library charges 30p each day a book is late. Ivy had one book that was 5 days late. If she had £5.81 before paying this fee, how much does she have after the fee is paid?

⑨ Henry has £2.73. He wants to buy a video game that costs £8.00. How much more money does he need?

⑩ Dylan picked fruit for two days. The farmer paid him £3.50 the first day and £4.25 the second day. How much did he earn all together?

⑪ Lexi had £7.82, then she bought a stuffed animal for £5.97. How much money does she have after the purchase?

⑫ Hannah has £6.40 and Edward has £8.21. How much more money does Edward have than Hannah?

Name: _____

Score:

Hamburger	Taco	Pie	Doughnut	Ice-Cream	Cookie
£4.97	£4.35	£3.50	£2.29	£1.15	£0.89

Use the images above to solve each problem.

① Hugo wants to buy a hamburger and a cookie. How much money will he need?

② Mia has eleven 20p, four 5p, and nine 1p coins. How much more money does she need to buy a slice of pie?

③ Jaxon orders a hamburger. His brother orders a taco. How much do their meals cost all together?

④ Esme wants to order a doughnut for herself and one for each of her two friends. How much money will she need?

⑤ Albert hands three 50p coins to the clerk and asks for an ice-cream cone. How much change should the clerk give Albert?

⑥ Isabelle has £8.72. She buys a taco and a doughnut. How much money does she have left?

Name: _____

Score:

What is it called?	① _____	② _____	③ _____	④ _____
What is its value?	⑤ £_____	⑥ £_____	⑦ £_____	⑧ £_____

Write the value of each group of notes.

£5   £2
£5   £1

⑨ £_____

£10   £5
£5   £1

⑩ £_____

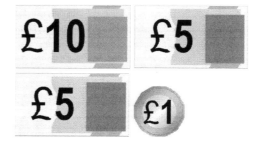

£5   £10
£10   £1
£5   £1

⑪ £_____

£10   £2
£10   £10
£5

⑫ £_____

Name: _____

Score:

Write the value of each group.

① £_____

② £_____

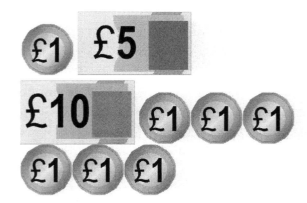

③ £_____

④ £_____

Write the value of each group.

⑤ 6 £10 notes
2 £5 notes
7 £1 coins   £_____

⑥ 4 £10 notes
4 £5 notes
2 £2 coins   £_____

⑦ 3 £10 notes
1 £5 notes
1 £2 coin
8 £1 coins   £_____

⑧ 7 £10 notes
3 £5 notes
1 £1 coin   £_____

⑨ 5 £10 notes
5 £5 notes
2 £2 coins
2 £1 coins   £_____

⑩ 2 £10 notes
11 £5 notes
4 £2 coins
4 £1 coins   £_____

Name: _____

Score:

Make each problem equivalent.

① 5 **20p** = ____ **£1**

② 1 **£1** = ____ **1p**

③ 6 **50p** = ____ **£1**

④ 1 **£1** = ____ **10p**

⑤ 1 **£1** = ____ **5p**

⑥ 3 **£5** = ____ **£1**

⑦ 1 **£5** = ____ **1p**

⑧ 1 **£5** = ____ **50p**

⑨ 10 **£5** = ____ **£10**

⑩ 40 **£10** = ____ **£2**

Name: _____

Score:

Write the value of each group.

£5 2p 1p 10p 20p
5p 10p 1p 10p

① £_____

£10 10p 50p
20p 20p 20p 20p 1p

② £_____

£10 £1
£5 20p 20p 5p

③ £_____

£2 1p 1p 10p 5p
5p 5p

④ £_____

£5 20p 20p 20p
£10 20p 20p 20p

⑤ £_____

£10 10p 2p
5p 1p 20p 1p

⑥ £_____

£10 £5
£10 £2 50p 10p
10p 10p 20p 20p 20p

⑦ £_____

£2 20p 5p £1
1p 20p £5

⑧ £_____

Name: _____

Score:

Subtract the following values. (Don't forget to include the dollar symbol.)

①	②	③	④	⑤
£62.48	£15.75	£53.39	£47.13	£90.42
−£8.93	−£4.16	−£15.27	−£17.63	−£36.77

Solve the following word problems.

⑥ Teddy was given £35 for his birthday. He bought a new baseball bat for £18.55. How much money does he have left?

⑦ Emily has £46.20. She wants to buy a new e-reader tablet. It costs £80. How much more money does she need to save?

⑧ Arlo has a £50 and a £20 note. Ken has £41.37. How much more money does Arlo have than Ken?

⑨ Freya has £8.26 and Clair has £26.07. How much money do they have together?

⑩ Henry wants to buy a shirt for £16.99 and socks for £5.75. How much will these items cost?

⑪ Evelyn had £14.71. She then received two £10 notes, a £5 note, and a £2 coin for her birthday. How much does she have now?

⑫ Elliot earns £15 every time he mows the lawn. He mows the lawn three times. How much more does he need to save to buy a skateboard that costs £72.45?

Name: _____

Score:

Bike

Scooter

Basketball

Baseball

£90.00   £45.00   £17.85   £7.00

Use the images above to solve each problem.

① Daisy Is saving her money for a scooter. If she has £17.64 now, how much more money will she need to save?

② David wants to buy a basketball and a baseball. How much money will he need?

③ Mr. Kelly wants to buy 4 baseballs for his gym class. How much money will he need?

④ Reuben wants to buy a bike. He currently has six £10 notes and twelve £1 coins. How much more money does he need?

⑤ Leo and his sister both want a scooter. How much money will they need to buy them?

⑥ How much more does a scooter cost than a basketball?

Day 21

Large Notes

Name: _____

£20   £50

What is it called?	① _____	② _____
What is its value?	③ £_____	④ £_____

Write the value of each group.

£1 £50

£20 £2 £2 £2

£10

⑤ £_____

£20 £50

£20 £50

⑥ £_____

£50 £50

£10 £50

£50

⑦ £_____

£10 £5

£50 £5

£50 £2 £1

⑧ £_____

Name: _____

Score:

Write the value of each group.

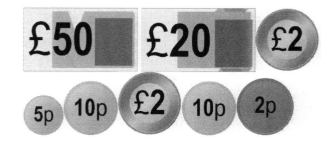

£50 £20 £2
5p 10p £2 10p 2p

£50 10p 20p 20p
20p 20p £2

① £_____

② £_____

£50 £50
£50 £20 20p
20p 10p £1 5p 10p

£20 £2 5p
£20 £1 10p

④ £_____

③ £_____

Write the value of each group.

⑤ 6 £10 notes
2 £5 notes
7 £1 coins   £_____
3 20p coins
2 10p coins

⑥ 2 £50 notes
4 £10 notes
1 £5 note   £_____
6 £2 coins
4 20p coins
1 5p coin

⑦ 1 £50 note
4 £20 notes
3 £10 notes   £_____
2 £1 coins
5 50p coins
5 10p coins
2 1p coins

⑧ 3 £50 notes
3 £20 notes
4 £5 notes   £_____
4 £2 notes
8 £1 notes
7 10p coins
8 2p coins

Name: _____

Score:

Find the equivalet value for each problem.

① 1 £20 = ____ £5

② 1 £50 = ____ £10

③ 2 £20 = ____ £2

④ 1 £20 = ____ £1

⑤ 1 £50 = ____ £5

Write the value for each group.

£50 £20 10p
£1 20p £2 £1 2p

£50 10p 20p 5p
20p 5p £1 10p

⑥ £_____

⑦ £_____

£20 £20 2p
£20 £2 20p 10p

£50 £1 50p 5p
£50 £2 10p

⑧ £_____

⑨ £_____

Name: _____

Subtract the following values. (Don't forget to include the dollar symbol.)

① £132.08
  −£47.10

② £401.29
  −£171.34

③ £685.98
  −£609.51

④ £200.00
  −£21.75

Solve the following word problems.

⑤ Sara is looking at computers. The first computer costs £349.50. The second costs £275.00. How much more is the first computer?

⑥ Sara wants the computer that costs £275.00. She currently has £190.45 saved. How much more money does she need to buy it?

⑦ Oscar was paid £250.00 for painting a house and £160.00 for painting the garage. How much money did he make?

⑧ Jack has £329.61 and Jerry has £570.15. How much more money does Jerry have than Jack?

⑨ Laura has four £50 notes, six £20 notes, and three £2 coins. How much money does she have?

⑩ Maria had £146.50 before buying concert tickets. If the tickets were £66.00, how much money does she have after the purchase?

⑪ Isaac and Josh want to buy an £800.00 fishing boat together. Isaac has £351.00 saved. Josh has £368.25 saved. How much more money do they need before they can buy the boat?

Day 25

Word Problems

Ring   Telescope   Motorized Scooter   Violin   Game Controller

£950.00   £675.00   £479.00   £320.00   £49.99

Use the images above to solve each problem.

① Joshua wants to buy 4 video game controllers. How much will he need for this purchase?

② Maryam wants to by a telescope. She currently has £426.00 saved. How much more money does she need to save?

③ Bella uses ten £50 notes to buy a motorized scooter. How much money should she receive in change?

④ Lucas wants to buy a diamond ring. He currently has £770.00 saved. How much more money does he need to buy the ring?

⑤ Max needs a new violin. He gives the clerk seven £50 notes. How much should he receive in change?

⑥ Amber also wants to buy a violin. She only has £20 notes. How many £20 notes will she need to buy the violin?

Day 26
Making Change

Name: _____

Score:

*Show how to make each value using the **fewest number of coins.***

① 19 pence:

___1___ ___1___ ___4___ _____

② 38 pence:

_____ _____ _____ _____

③ 61 pence:

_____ _____ _____ _____

④ 97 pence:

_____ _____ _____ _____

⑤ 83 pence:

_____ _____ _____ _____

⑥ 56 pence:

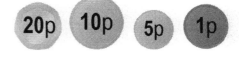

_____ _____ _____ _____

⑦ 24 pence:

_____ _____ _____ _____

⑧ 45 pence:

_____ _____ _____ _____

⑨ 72 pence:

_____ _____ _____ _____

⑩ 33 pence:

_____ _____ _____ _____

⑪ 26 pence:

_____ _____ _____ _____

⑫ 90 pence:

_____ _____ _____ _____

Day 27
Making Change

Name: _____

Score:

*Show how to make each value using the **fewest number of notes and coins.***

① £64.30

② £9.65

③ £17.90

④ £32.20

⑤ £98.40

⑥ £81.55

Day 28
Making Change

Name: _____

*Show how to make each value using the **fewest number of notes and coins.***

① £22.55

£10 _____

£5 _____

£1   20p   10p   5p

_____

② £63.15

£10 _____

£5 _____

£1   20p   10p   5p

_____

③ £48.90

£10 _____

£5 _____

£1   20p   10p   5p

_____

④ £39.70

£10 _____

£5 _____

£1   20p   10p   5p

_____

⑤ £50.50

£10 _____

£5 _____

£1   20p   10p   5p

_____

⑥ £76.85

£10 _____

£5 _____

£1   20p   10p   5p

_____

Name: _____

Score:

Complete the fraction to represent each image.

①  $\dfrac{2}{}$

②  $\dfrac{}{2}$

③ 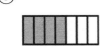 $\dfrac{}{7}$

④ 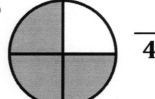 $\dfrac{}{4}$

⑤ 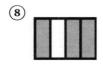 $\dfrac{4}{}$

⑥ 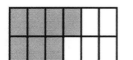 $\dfrac{}{8}$

⑦  $\dfrac{3}{}$

⑧ $\dfrac{3}{}$

⑨ 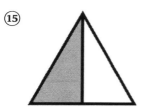 $\dfrac{}{12}$

⑩ 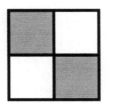 $\dfrac{}{4}$

⑪ 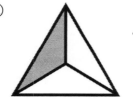 $\dfrac{1}{}$

⑫ 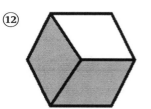 $\dfrac{}{3}$

⑬  $\dfrac{}{6}$

⑭ 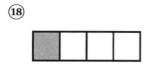 $\dfrac{7}{}$

⑮ 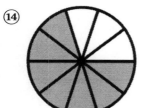 $\dfrac{1}{}$

⑯ $\dfrac{}{3}$

⑰ 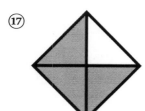 $\dfrac{3}{}$

⑱  $\dfrac{}{4}$

Day 30
Identifying Fractions

Name: _____

Score:

Write the fraction that represents each image.

①  ___

②  ___

③ 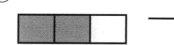 ___

④ 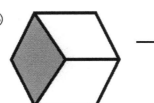 ___

⑤  ___

⑥ 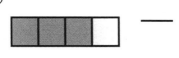 ___

⑦ 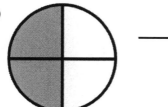 ___

⑧  ___

⑨ 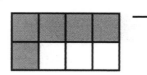 ___

⑩  ___

⑪  ___

⑫  ___

⑬ 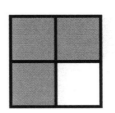 ___

⑭ 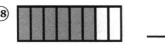 ___

⑮ 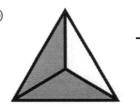 ___

⑯ 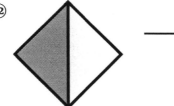 ___

⑰  ___

⑱ 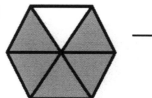 ___

Name: _____

Score:

Problems 1-6: *Answer each question by writing your answer in fraction form.*

①

How many of the flowers are dark? _____

②

How many cupcakes have sprinkles? _____

③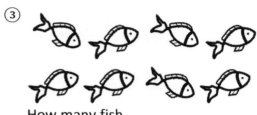

How many fish
are swimming down? _____

④

How many ice-creams
are chocolate flavored? _____

⑤

How many candies have stripes? _____

⑥

How many of the shells are white? _____

Problems 7-10: *Write your answer in the blank space provided to make each equation true.*

⑦

$\frac{1}{3}$ of 3 is ____.

⑧

$\frac{3}{4}$ of 4 is ____.

⑨

$\frac{1}{2}$ of 12 is ____.

⑩

$\frac{2}{5}$ of 15 is ____.

Name: _____

Score:

Problems 1-9: *Write the fraction that represents each image.*

① ___

②  ___

③ 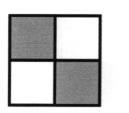 ___

④  ___

⑤ 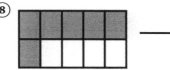 ___

⑥  ___

⑦ 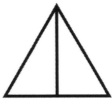 ___

⑧  ___

⑨ 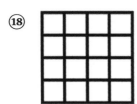 ___

Problems 10-18: *Shade each shape to represents the fraction to the right.*

⑩ 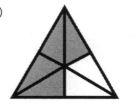 $\dfrac{2}{8}$

⑪  $\dfrac{1}{3}$

⑫  $\dfrac{6}{7}$

⑬  $\dfrac{1}{2}$

⑭  $\dfrac{1}{5}$

⑮ 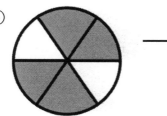 $\dfrac{5}{10}$

⑯ 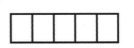 $\dfrac{4}{5}$

⑰  $\dfrac{2}{3}$

⑱  $\dfrac{11}{16}$

Day 33

Name: _____

Score:

Problems 1-7: *Answer each question by writing your answer in fraction form.*

① *Draw circles around the dots to divide them into 2 equal groups.*

What is $\frac{1}{2}$ of 10? _____

② *Draw circles around the dots to divide them into 5 equal groups.*

What is $\frac{3}{5}$ of 15? _____

③ *Draw circles around the dots to divide them into 4 equal groups.*

What is $\frac{1}{4}$ of 20? _____

④ *Draw circles around the dots to divide them into 3 equal groups.*

What is $\frac{2}{3}$ of 12? _____

⑤ *Draw circles around the dots to divide them into 4 equal groups.*

What is $\frac{3}{4}$ of 8? _____

⑥ *Draw circles around the dots to divide them into 2 equal groups.*

What is $\frac{1}{2}$ of 16? _____

⑦ *Draw circles around the dots to divide them into 6 equal groups.*

What is $\frac{5}{6}$ of 18? _____

Name: _____

Score:

Problems 1-4: *Answer each question by writing your answer in fraction form.*

①

How many faces are happy? _____

②

How many faces are wearing a hat? _____

③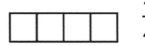

How many bikers have
one tire off the ground? _____

④

How many delivery trucks are there? _____

Problems 5-13: *Shade each shape to represents the fraction to the right.*

⑤ $\dfrac{2}{4}$

⑥ $\dfrac{1}{2}$

⑦  $\dfrac{1}{5}$

⑧  $\dfrac{6}{8}$

⑨  $\dfrac{3}{12}$

⑩ $\dfrac{2}{3}$

⑪  $\dfrac{5}{6}$

⑫  $\dfrac{1}{4}$

⑬  $\dfrac{9}{10}$

Name: _____

Score:

Write the fraction that represents each image.

①  ___

②  ___

③  ___

④ 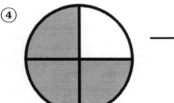 ___

⑤  ___

⑥  ___

⑦ 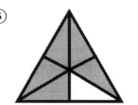 ___

⑧ 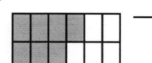 ___

⑨  ___

Problems 10-13: Write your answer in the blank space provided to make each equation true.

⑩

$\frac{2}{5}$ of 5 is _____.

⑪

$\frac{3}{4}$ of 8 is _____.

⑫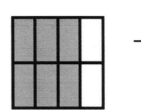

$\frac{1}{2}$ of 6 is _____.

⑬

$\frac{1}{4}$ of 16 is _____.

Name: _____

Score:

Problems 1-6: *Answer each question by writing your answer in fraction form.*

① *Draw circles around the dots to divide them into 3 equal groups.*

What is $\frac{2}{3}$ of 9? _____

② *Draw circles around the dots to divide them into 4 equal groups.*

What is $\frac{1}{4}$ of 24? _____

③ *Draw circles around the dots to divide them into 5 equal groups.*

What is $\frac{3}{5}$ of 25? _____

④ *Draw circles around the dots to divide them into 8 equal groups.*

What is $\frac{7}{8}$ of 16? _____

⑤ *Draw circles around the dots to divide them into 4 equal groups.*

What is $\frac{3}{4}$ of 12? _____

⑥ *Draw circles around the dots to divide them into 2 equal groups.*

What is $\frac{5}{6}$ of 24? _____

⑦ *Draw circles around the dots to divide them into 3 equal groups.*

What is $\frac{1}{3}$ of 6? _____

Name: _____

Score:

Problems 1-6: *Is the fraction on the right greater than (>), less than (<), or equal to (=) the fraction on the left? Look at each shape to help you decide.*

① $\dfrac{1}{3}$ ____ $\dfrac{2}{3}$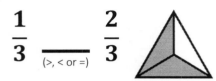
(>, < or =)

② $\dfrac{4}{5}$ ____ $\dfrac{4}{5}$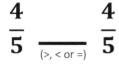
(>, < or =)

③ $\dfrac{6}{8}$ ____ $\dfrac{4}{8}$
(>, < or =)

④ $\dfrac{3}{6}$ ____ $\dfrac{2}{6}$
(>, < or =)

⑤ $\dfrac{2}{4}$ ____ $\dfrac{3}{4}$
(>, < or =)

⑥ $\dfrac{6}{10}$ ____ $\dfrac{4}{10}$
(>, < or =)

⑦ $\dfrac{1}{3}$ ____ $\dfrac{1}{3}$
(>, < or =)

⑧ 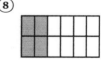 $\dfrac{4}{12}$ ____ $\dfrac{7}{12}$
(>, < or =)

⑨ $\dfrac{2}{4}$ ____ $\dfrac{2}{4}$
(>, < or =)

⑩ $\dfrac{4}{6}$ ____ $\dfrac{3}{6}$
(>, < or =)

⑪ $\dfrac{2}{8}$ ____ $\dfrac{5}{8}$
(>, < or =)

⑫ $\dfrac{3}{5}$ ____ $\dfrac{3}{5}$
(>, < or =)

Day 38
Equivalent Fractions

Name: _____

Score:

Problems 1-6: *Write your answer in the blank space provided to make each equation true.*

① 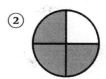 $\dfrac{1}{2} = \dfrac{}{4}$

② $\dfrac{}{4} = \dfrac{6}{8}$

③ 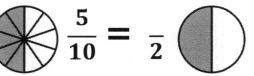 $\dfrac{5}{10} = \dfrac{}{2}$

④ 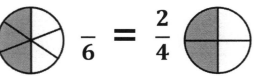 $\dfrac{4}{6} = \dfrac{}{3}$

⑤ 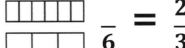 $\dfrac{}{6} = \dfrac{2}{4}$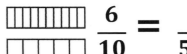

⑥ 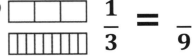 $\dfrac{2}{8} = \dfrac{}{4}$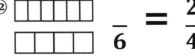

Problems 7-14: *Shade the shapes below to determine the equivalent fraction. Write your answer in the blank space provided to make each equation true.*

⑦ 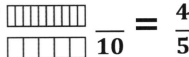 $\dfrac{3}{4} = \dfrac{}{8}$

⑧ $\dfrac{3}{6} = \dfrac{}{2}$

⑨ $\dfrac{}{6} = \dfrac{2}{3}$

⑩ $\dfrac{6}{10} = \dfrac{}{5}$

⑪ $\dfrac{1}{3} = \dfrac{}{9}$

⑫ $\dfrac{}{6} = \dfrac{2}{4}$

⑬ $\dfrac{}{10} = \dfrac{4}{5}$

⑭ $\dfrac{1}{4} = \dfrac{}{8}$

Day 39

> < =

Name: _____

Score:

Problems 1-6: *Is the fraction on the right greater than (>), less than (<), or equal to (=) the fraction on the left? Look at each shape to help you decide.*

① $\dfrac{2}{4}$ ___ $\dfrac{2}{4}$
(>, < or =)

② 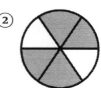 $\dfrac{4}{6}$ ___ $\dfrac{3}{6}$
(>, < or =)

③ $\dfrac{2}{5}$ ___ $\dfrac{4}{5}$
(>, < or =)

④ 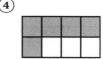 $\dfrac{5}{8}$ ___ $\dfrac{6}{8}$
(>, < or =)

⑤ $\dfrac{2}{4}$ ___ $\dfrac{1}{4}$
(>, < or =)

⑥ $\dfrac{2}{6}$ ___ $\dfrac{2}{6}$
(>, < or =)

Problems 7-14: *Decided if the fraction on the right is greater than (>), less than (<), or equal to (=) the fraction on the left. Shade the shapes to help you make your decision.*

⑦ 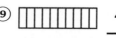 $\dfrac{1}{2}$ ___ $\dfrac{1}{4}$
(>, < or =)

⑧ 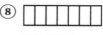 $\dfrac{4}{7}$ ___ $\dfrac{2}{5}$
(>, < or =)

⑨  $\dfrac{4}{10}$ ___ $\dfrac{2}{3}$
(>, < or =)

⑩ 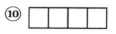 $\dfrac{2}{4}$ ___ $\dfrac{3}{6}$
(>, < or =)

⑪ $\dfrac{6}{8}$ ___ $\dfrac{1}{2}$
(>, < or =)

⑫ $\dfrac{1}{3}$ ___ $\dfrac{2}{4}$
(>, < or =)

⑬  $\dfrac{8}{10}$ ___ $\dfrac{4}{5}$
(>, < or =)

⑭ 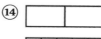 $\dfrac{1}{2}$ ___ $\dfrac{2}{5}$
(>, < or =)

Day 40

Mixed Numbers

Name: _____

Score:

Problems 1-5: *Shade the shapes to represents each fraction. (You may not need all the shapes to represent the fraction).*

① $4\frac{1}{2}$

② $6\frac{2}{3}$

③ $2\frac{5}{6}$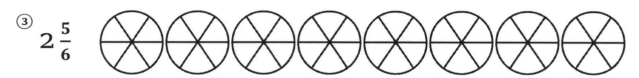

④ $\frac{1}{4}$

⑤ $3\frac{1}{3}$

Problems 6-10: *Write a fraction to represent the amount of shaded shapes.*

⑥ _____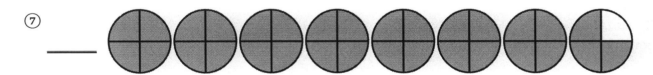

⑦ _____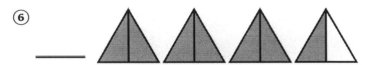

⑧ _____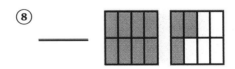

⑨ _____

⑩ _____

Name: _____

Problems 1-6: *Is the fraction on the right greater than (>), less than (<), or equal to (=) the fraction on the left? Look at the shapes to help you decide.*

① 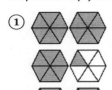 $5\frac{1}{6}$ _____ $3\frac{5}{6}$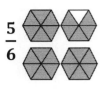
(>, < or =)

② 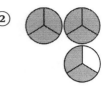 $2\frac{2}{3}$ _____ $4\frac{2}{3}$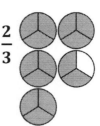
(>, < or =)

③ $1\frac{3}{4}$ _____ $1\frac{2}{4}$
(>, < or =)

④ 4 _____ $2\frac{1}{2}$
(>, < or =)

⑤ $1\frac{1}{8}$ _____ $\frac{7}{8}$
(>, < or =)

⑥ 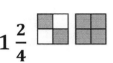 $3\frac{2}{4}$ _____ $2\frac{2}{4}$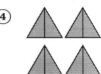
(>, < or =)

Problems 7-14: *Decided if the fraction on the right is greater than (>), less than (<), or equal to (=) the fraction on the left. Draw your own shapes to help figure out the answer.*

⑦ $3\frac{4}{5}$ _____ $6\frac{1}{3}$
(>, < or =)

⑧ $3\frac{2}{3}$ _____ $3\frac{2}{5}$
(>, < or =)

⑨ $2\frac{1}{2}$ _____ $1\frac{3}{4}$
(>, < or =)

⑩ $2\frac{2}{4}$ _____ $2\frac{1}{3}$
(>, < or =)

⑪ $3\frac{5}{6}$ _____ $5\frac{1}{8}$
(>, < or =)

⑫ $\frac{3}{5}$ _____ $2\frac{1}{5}$
(>, < or =)

⑬ $8\frac{1}{8}$ _____ $4\frac{1}{2}$
(>, < or =)

⑭ $5\frac{4}{6}$ _____ $5\frac{2}{3}$
(>, < or =)

Name: _____

Problems 1-4: *Is the fraction on the right greater than (>), less than (<), or equal to (=) the fraction on the left? Look at the shapes to help you decide. Draw your own shapes if it helps you figure out the answer.*

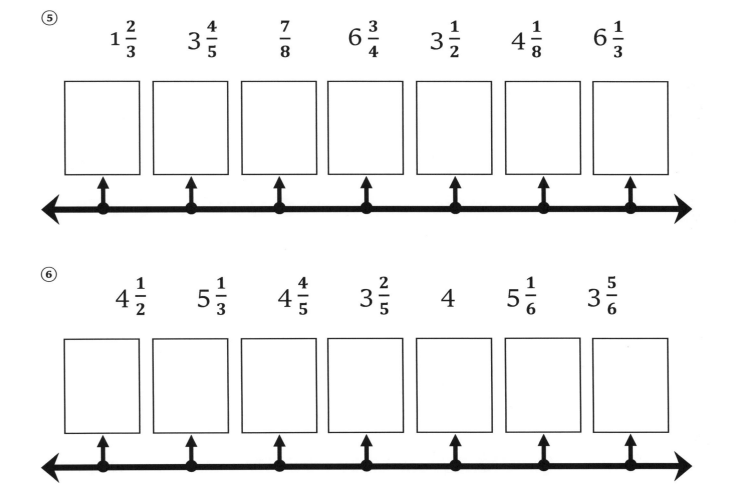

① $5\frac{1}{6}$ _____ $3\frac{5}{6}$
(>, < or =)

② $2\frac{2}{3}$ _____ $4\frac{2}{3}$
(>, < or =)

③ $3\frac{4}{5}$ _____ $6\frac{1}{3}$
(>, < or =)

④ $3\frac{2}{3}$ _____ $3\frac{2}{5}$
(>, < or =)

Problems 5-6: *Write the fractions in order from smallest to largest.*

⑤ $1\frac{2}{3}$ $3\frac{4}{5}$ $\frac{7}{8}$ $6\frac{3}{4}$ $3\frac{1}{2}$ $4\frac{1}{8}$ $6\frac{1}{3}$

⑥ $4\frac{1}{2}$ $5\frac{1}{3}$ $4\frac{4}{5}$ $3\frac{2}{5}$ 4 $5\frac{1}{6}$ $3\frac{5}{6}$

Day 43
Adding Fractions

Name: _____

Score:

Problems 1-6: *Shade the third image and then write the correct numerator to make the answer true.*

①

$$\frac{3}{8} + \frac{3}{8} = \frac{}{8}$$

②

$$\frac{2}{5} + \frac{1}{5} = \frac{}{5}$$

③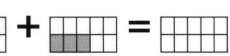

$$\frac{4}{10} + \frac{3}{10} = \frac{}{10}$$

④

$$\frac{2}{6} + \frac{2}{6} = \frac{}{6}$$

⑤

$$\frac{1}{4} + \frac{2}{4} = \frac{}{4}$$

⑥

$$\frac{1}{3} + \frac{1}{3} = \frac{}{3}$$

Problems 7-10: *Shade the three images and then write the correct numerator to make each answer true.*

⑦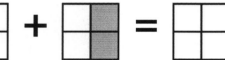

$$\frac{1}{3} + \frac{1}{3} = \frac{}{3}$$

⑧

$$\frac{3}{5} + \frac{1}{5} = \frac{}{5}$$

⑨

$$\frac{5}{12} + \frac{4}{12} = \frac{}{12}$$

⑩

$$\frac{2}{6} + \frac{2}{6} = \frac{}{6}$$

Day 44
Adding Fractions

Name: _____

Score:

Problems 1-4: *Shade the three images and then write the correct fraction to make each answer true.*

①
$$\frac{1}{6} + \frac{2}{6} = \frac{-}{-}$$

②
$$\frac{2}{4} + \frac{2}{4} = \frac{-}{-}$$

③
$$\frac{10}{16} + \frac{3}{16} = \frac{-}{-}$$

④
$$\frac{2}{8} + \frac{3}{8} = \frac{-}{-}$$

Problems 5-19: *Add each set of fractions.*

⑤ $\dfrac{3}{9} + \dfrac{4}{9} =$

⑥ $\dfrac{2}{5} + \dfrac{2}{5} =$

⑦ $\dfrac{1}{6} + \dfrac{4}{6} =$

⑧ $\dfrac{7}{15} + \dfrac{4}{15} =$

⑨ $\dfrac{2}{3} + \dfrac{1}{3} =$

⑩ $\dfrac{3}{8} + \dfrac{3}{8} =$

⑪ $\dfrac{7}{10} + \dfrac{4}{10} =$

⑫ $\dfrac{2}{7} + \dfrac{4}{7} =$

⑬ $\dfrac{2}{4} + \dfrac{1}{4} =$

⑭ $\dfrac{2}{6} + \dfrac{3}{6} =$

⑮ $\dfrac{4}{9} + \dfrac{2}{9} =$

⑯ $\dfrac{2}{5} + \dfrac{3}{5} =$

⑰ $\dfrac{1}{11} + \dfrac{1}{11} =$

⑱ $\dfrac{2}{8} + \dfrac{2}{8} =$

⑲ $\dfrac{3}{7} + \dfrac{3}{7} =$

Day 45
Subtracting Fractions

Name: _____

Score:

Problems 1-6: *Shade the third image and then write the correct numerator to make each answer true.*

①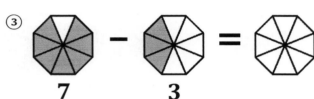

$$\frac{4}{5} - \frac{2}{5} = \frac{}{5}$$

②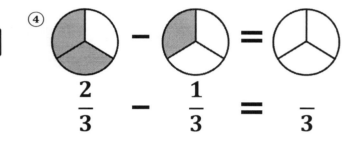

$$\frac{2}{4} - \frac{1}{4} = \frac{}{4}$$

③

$$\frac{7}{8} - \frac{3}{8} = \frac{}{8}$$

④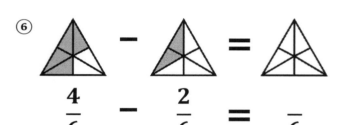

$$\frac{2}{3} - \frac{1}{3} = \frac{}{3}$$

⑤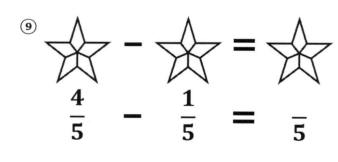

$$\frac{10}{10} - \frac{7}{10} = \frac{}{10}$$

⑥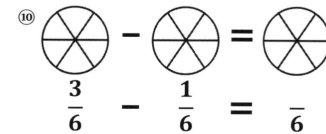

$$\frac{4}{6} - \frac{2}{6} = \frac{}{6}$$

Problems 7-10: *Shade the three images and then write the correct numerator to make each answer true.*

⑦

$$\frac{3}{4} - \frac{1}{4} = \frac{}{4}$$

⑧

$$\frac{6}{8} - \frac{3}{8} = \frac{}{8}$$

⑨

$$\frac{4}{5} - \frac{1}{5} = \frac{}{5}$$

⑩

$$\frac{3}{6} - \frac{1}{6} = \frac{}{6}$$

Day 46
Subtracting Fractions

Name: _____

Score:

Problems 1-4: *Shade the three images and then write the correct fraction to make each answer true.*

① $\dfrac{2}{6} - \dfrac{1}{6} = \dfrac{}{}$

② $\dfrac{2}{4} - \dfrac{2}{4} = \dfrac{}{}$

③ $\dfrac{10}{16} - \dfrac{3}{16} = \dfrac{}{}$

④ $\dfrac{5}{8} - \dfrac{2}{8} = \dfrac{}{}$

Problems 5-9: *Subtract each set of fractions.*

⑤ $\dfrac{4}{6} - \dfrac{1}{6} =$

⑥ $\dfrac{5}{9} - \dfrac{1}{9} =$

⑦ $\dfrac{4}{5} - \dfrac{3}{5} =$

⑧ $\dfrac{8}{10} - \dfrac{4}{10} =$

⑨ $\dfrac{11}{12} - \dfrac{2}{12} =$

⑩ $\dfrac{7}{8} - \dfrac{3}{8} =$

⑪ $\dfrac{3}{4} - \dfrac{2}{4} =$

⑫ $\dfrac{5}{7} - \dfrac{3}{7} =$

⑬ $\dfrac{2}{3} - \dfrac{1}{3} =$

⑭ $\dfrac{13}{16} - \dfrac{2}{16} =$

⑮ $\dfrac{7}{10} - \dfrac{5}{10} =$

⑯ $\dfrac{2}{5} - \dfrac{1}{5} =$

⑰ $\dfrac{5}{6} - \dfrac{4}{6} =$

⑱ $\dfrac{5}{8} - \dfrac{2}{8} =$

⑲ $\dfrac{8}{9} - \dfrac{1}{9} =$

Score:

Name: _____

Problems 1-7: *Add each set of mixed fractions.*

①

$3\frac{5}{8}$ **+** $1\frac{1}{8}$ **=** _____

②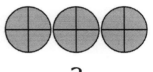

3 **+** $1\frac{3}{4}$ **=** _____

③

$3\frac{1}{3}$ **+** $2\frac{2}{3}$ **=** _____

④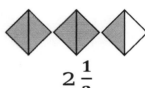

$2\frac{1}{2}$ **+** 3 **=** _____

⑤

$2\frac{2}{6}$ **+** $\frac{3}{6}$ **=** _____

⑥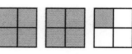

$2\frac{1}{4}$ **+** $2\frac{2}{4}$ **=** _____

⑦

1 **+** $2\frac{1}{2}$ **=** _____

Name: _____

Score:

Problems 1-4: *Shade the images to represent each fraction, then add each set of fractions.*

①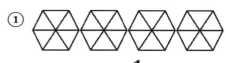

$3\frac{1}{6}$ + 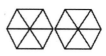 2 = ____

②

1 + $\frac{1}{2}$ = ____

③

$1\frac{2}{5}$ +  $2\frac{2}{5}$ = ____

④

2 + 2 = ____

Problems 5-16: *Add each set of fractions*

⑤ $5\frac{2}{4} + 3\frac{1}{4} =$

⑥ $4\frac{3}{6} + 2\frac{2}{6} =$

⑦ $1\frac{1}{3} + 7\frac{1}{3} =$

⑧ $2\frac{2}{7} + 3 =$

⑨ $6\frac{2}{5} + 5\frac{2}{5} =$

⑩ $1\frac{3}{16} + 4\frac{7}{16} =$

⑪ $2\frac{1}{4} + 2\frac{1}{4} =$

⑫ $5\frac{2}{8} + 1\frac{3}{8} =$

⑬ $8 + 4\frac{1}{2} =$

⑭ $2\frac{2}{7} + 3\frac{3}{7} =$

⑮ $4\frac{2}{9} + 1\frac{6}{9} =$

⑯ $3\frac{3}{10} + 3\frac{3}{10} =$

Day 49
Adding Mixed Numbers

Name: _____

Score:

Problems 1-7: *Add each set of mixed fractions.*

①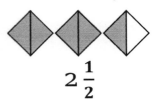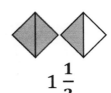

$2\frac{1}{2}$ **+** $1\frac{1}{2}$ **=** _____

②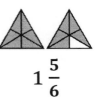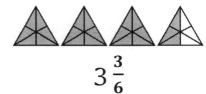

$1\frac{5}{6}$ **+** $3\frac{3}{6}$ **=** _____

③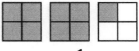

$2\frac{1}{4}$ **+** $2\frac{3}{4}$ **=** _____

④

$3\frac{1}{2}$ **+** $3\frac{1}{2}$ **=** _____

⑤

$3\frac{2}{3}$ **+** $\frac{2}{3}$ **=** _____

⑥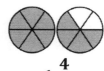

$1\frac{5}{6}$ **+** $1\frac{4}{6}$ **=** _____

⑦

$1\frac{3}{8}$ **+** $2\frac{5}{8}$ **=** _____

Name: _____

Score:

Problems 1-4: *Shade the images to represent each fraction, then add each set of fractions.*

① 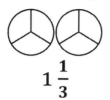 $1\frac{1}{3}$ **+** 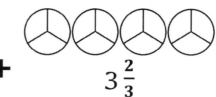 $3\frac{2}{3}$ **=** _____

② 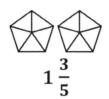 $2\frac{3}{4}$ **+** 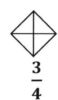 $\frac{3}{4}$ **=** _____

③ 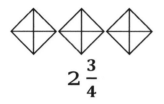 $1\frac{3}{5}$ **+** 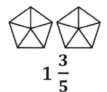 $1\frac{3}{5}$ **=** _____

④ 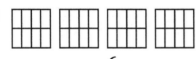 $3\frac{6}{8}$ **+** $3\frac{7}{8}$ **=** _____

Problems 5-16: *Add each set of fractions*

⑤ $1\frac{2}{4} + 6\frac{3}{4} =$ ⑥ $4\frac{4}{7} + 2\frac{5}{7} =$ ⑦ $1\frac{2}{3} + \frac{1}{3} =$

⑧ $2\frac{1}{2} + 2\frac{1}{2} =$ ⑨ $6\frac{5}{9} + 5\frac{5}{9} =$ ⑩ $7\frac{11}{12} + 3\frac{8}{12} =$

⑪ $6\frac{4}{5} + 2\frac{3}{5} =$ ⑫ $1\frac{2}{8} + 5\frac{6}{8} =$ ⑬ $2\frac{2}{3} + 9\frac{2}{3} =$

⑭ $4\frac{4}{6} + 8\frac{3}{6} =$ ⑮ $1\frac{1}{2} + 1\frac{1}{2} =$ ⑯ $3\frac{3}{4} + 6\frac{3}{4} =$

Day 51

Name: _____

Score:

Problems 1-27: *Add each set of fractions*

① $5\frac{3}{7} + 3\frac{3}{7} =$

② $4\frac{1}{3} + 7\frac{2}{3} =$

③ $8\frac{1}{2} + 2\frac{1}{2} =$

④ $2\frac{1}{9} + 1\frac{5}{9} =$

⑤ $6\frac{2}{4} + 3\frac{3}{4} =$

⑥ $1\frac{2}{5} + 1\frac{4}{5} =$

⑦ $4\frac{3}{8} + 4\frac{6}{8} =$

⑧ $2\frac{4}{8} + 3\frac{1}{8} =$

⑨ $9\frac{2}{6} + 7\frac{4}{6} =$

⑩ $5\frac{4}{7} + 2\frac{2}{7} =$

⑪ $7\frac{1}{2} + 2\frac{1}{2} =$

⑫ $4\frac{1}{5} + 3\frac{2}{5} =$

⑬ $8\frac{3}{4} + 5\frac{3}{4} =$

⑭ $6\frac{2}{7} + 6\frac{5}{7} =$

⑮ $2\frac{3}{5} + 2\frac{3}{5} =$

⑯ $7\frac{1}{2} + 1\frac{1}{2} =$

⑰ $4\frac{2}{3} + \frac{1}{3} =$

⑱ $1\frac{5}{12} + 5\frac{5}{12} =$

⑲ $4\frac{2}{7} + 2\frac{3}{7} =$

⑳ $8\frac{1}{2} + 1\frac{1}{2} =$

㉑ $5\frac{1}{3} + 5\frac{2}{3} =$

㉒ $\frac{6}{9} + 3\frac{4}{9} =$

㉓ $6\frac{4}{5} + 2\frac{3}{5} =$

㉔ $3\frac{2}{4} + 6\frac{1}{4} =$

㉕ $7\frac{4}{8} + 5\frac{6}{8} =$

㉖ $3\frac{4}{6} + 8\frac{2}{6} =$

㉗ $4\frac{1}{3} + 4\frac{1}{3} =$

Name: _____

Score:

Problems1-7: *Subtract each set of fractions*

①

$2\frac{1}{2}$ −  $1\frac{1}{2}$ = _____

②

$3\frac{2}{3}$ − $1\frac{1}{3}$ = _____

③

$3\frac{4}{5}$ − 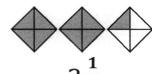 $\frac{2}{5}$ = _____

④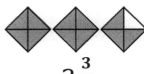

$2\frac{3}{4}$ − 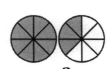 $2\frac{1}{4}$ = _____

⑤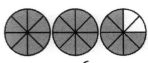

$3\frac{6}{8}$ − $1\frac{3}{8}$ = _____

⑥

$1\frac{1}{2}$ − $1\frac{1}{2}$ = _____

⑦

$2\frac{5}{10}$ − $1\frac{1}{10}$ = _____

Name: _____

Score:

Problems 1-4: *Shade the images to represent each fraction, then subtract each set of fractions.*

①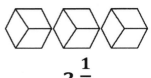

$2\dfrac{1}{3}$ — $1\dfrac{1}{3}$ = _____

②

$1\dfrac{3}{4}$ — $1\dfrac{1}{4}$ = _____

③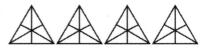

$3\dfrac{5}{6}$ — $1\dfrac{3}{6}$ = _____

④

$1\dfrac{4}{5}$ — $1\dfrac{2}{5}$ = _____

Problems 5-16: *Subtract each set of fractions.*

⑤ $8\dfrac{6}{7} - 5\dfrac{3}{7} =$

⑥ $9\dfrac{3}{4} - 3\dfrac{1}{4} =$

⑦ $4\dfrac{5}{8} - 3\dfrac{2}{8} =$

⑧ $6\dfrac{1}{3} - 2\dfrac{1}{3} =$

⑨ $3\dfrac{6}{9} - 1\dfrac{4}{9} =$

⑩ $8\dfrac{3}{5} - 4\dfrac{3}{5} =$

⑪ $7\dfrac{7}{8} - 1\dfrac{4}{8} =$

⑫ $2\dfrac{4}{5} - \dfrac{3}{5} =$

⑬ $5\dfrac{8}{10} - 3\dfrac{4}{10} =$

⑭ $6\dfrac{2}{4} - 4\dfrac{2}{4} =$

⑮ $3\dfrac{2}{7} - 1\dfrac{1}{7} =$

⑯ $8\dfrac{5}{6} - 2\dfrac{3}{6} =$

Name: _____

Score:

Problems 1-7: *Subtract each set of fractions*

① 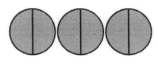   

3 $-$ $2\frac{1}{2}$ $=$ _____

② 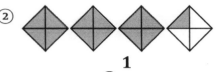

$3\frac{1}{4}$ $-$ $1\frac{3}{4}$ $=$ _____

③ 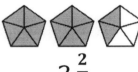

$2\frac{2}{5}$ $-$ $\frac{3}{5}$ $=$ _____

④    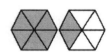

3 $-$ $1\frac{2}{6}$ $=$ _____

⑤ 

$3\frac{1}{3}$ $-$ $\frac{1}{3}$ $=$ _____

⑥

$1\frac{4}{8}$ $-$ $\frac{6}{8}$ $=$ _____

⑦ 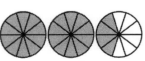   

$2\frac{4}{10}$ $-$ $1\frac{7}{10}$ $=$ _____

Problems 1-4: *Shade the images to represent each fraction, then subtract each set of fractions.*

①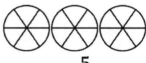

$$3\frac{2}{5} \quad - \quad 1\frac{3}{5} \quad = \quad \underline{\hspace{1cm}}$$

②

$$2 \quad - \quad 1\frac{2}{4} \quad = \quad \underline{\hspace{1cm}}$$

③

$$2\frac{1}{3} \quad - \quad \frac{2}{3} \quad = \quad \underline{\hspace{1cm}}$$

④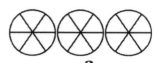

$$2\frac{5}{6} \quad - \quad 2\frac{3}{6} \quad = \quad \underline{\hspace{1cm}}$$

Problems 5-16: *Subtract each set of fractions.*

⑤ $5\frac{2}{6} - 3\frac{3}{6} =$ ⑥ $4\frac{1}{4} - 1\frac{2}{4} =$ ⑦ $9 - 2\frac{1}{2} =$

⑧ $3\frac{1}{5} - \frac{3}{5} =$ ⑨ $8\frac{3}{7} - 7\frac{5}{7} =$ ⑩ $6\frac{1}{4} - 1\frac{3}{4} =$

⑪ $9\frac{5}{9} - 1\frac{8}{9} =$ ⑫ $5 - 2\frac{2}{3} =$ ⑬ $8\frac{1}{6} - 6\frac{5}{6} =$

⑭ $7\frac{2}{4} - 2\frac{3}{4} =$ ⑮ $2\frac{3}{8} - 1\frac{7}{8} =$ ⑯ $12\frac{1}{5} - 5\frac{3}{5} =$

Day 56
Subtracting Mixed Numbers

Name: _____

Score:

Problems 1-27: *Subtract each set of fractions.*

① $7\frac{3}{5} - 1\frac{4}{5} =$

② $6\frac{1}{2} - 2\frac{1}{2} =$

③ $2\frac{4}{7} - \frac{6}{7} =$

④ $6\frac{2}{3} - 4\frac{1}{3} =$

⑤ $8\frac{5}{9} - 2\frac{1}{9} =$

⑥ $3\frac{2}{8} - 1\frac{5}{8} =$

⑦ $4\frac{1}{4} - 3\frac{3}{4} =$

⑧ $8\frac{5}{6} - 5\frac{3}{6} =$

⑨ $9 - 3\frac{1}{4} =$

⑩ $8\frac{3}{9} - 4\frac{7}{9} =$

⑪ $3\frac{6}{7} - 1\frac{4}{7} =$

⑫ $5\frac{6}{10} - 3\frac{8}{10} =$

⑬ $5\frac{2}{7} - 3\frac{2}{7} =$

⑭ $6 - 2\frac{1}{2} =$

⑮ $4\frac{3}{5} - 1\frac{2}{5} =$

⑯ $2\frac{2}{4} - 1\frac{3}{4} =$

⑰ $7\frac{1}{8} - 2\frac{7}{8} =$

⑱ $11\frac{1}{3} - 7 =$

⑲ $8\frac{3}{6} - 3\frac{5}{6} =$

⑳ $3\frac{2}{9} - \frac{5}{9} =$

㉑ $6\frac{1}{5} - 1\frac{3}{5} =$

㉒ $8\frac{1}{3} - 6\frac{1}{3} =$

㉓ $9\frac{6}{7} - 1\frac{5}{7} =$

㉔ $9 - 2\frac{4}{7} =$

㉕ $8\frac{1}{5} - 7\frac{3}{5} =$

㉖ $3\frac{3}{4} - 1\frac{3}{4} =$

㉗ $6\frac{2}{6} - 4\frac{5}{6} =$

© Libro Studio LLC 2020

Name: _Dylan_

Problems 1-4: Shade the circle with the correct answer.

1. Ⓐ 8:00
   Ⓑ 5:00 ✓
   Ⓒ 12:00
   Ⓓ 3:00

2. Ⓐ 7:00
   Ⓑ 11:00
   Ⓒ 1:00
   Ⓓ 12:00 ✓

3. Ⓐ 6:00 ✓
   Ⓑ 10:00
   Ⓒ 2:00
   Ⓓ 5:00

4. Ⓐ 4:00
   Ⓑ 5:00
   Ⓒ 11:00
   Ⓓ 1:00 ✓

Problems 5-8: Write the correct time on the line beneath each clock.

5. _8:00_

6. _10:00_

7. _3:00_ ✓

8. _1:00_ ✓

Problems 9-12: Draw hands on each clock so they represent the corresponding times.

9. _1:00_

10. _4:00_

11. _11:00_

12. _2:00_

Name: _____

Score:

Problems 1-4: Shade the circle with the correct answer.

1. Ⓐ 11:00
    Ⓑ 3:00
    Ⓒ 4:00 ✓
    Ⓓ 7:00

2. Ⓐ 10:00 ✓
    Ⓑ 11:00
    Ⓒ 5:00
    Ⓓ 2:00

3. Ⓐ 12:00
    Ⓑ 7:00
    Ⓒ 8:00 ✓
    Ⓓ 6:00

4. Ⓐ 8:00
    Ⓑ 9:00
    Ⓒ 7:00 ✓
    Ⓓ 10:00

Problems 5-8: Write the correct time on the line beneath each clock.

5. 12:00 ✓

6. 5:00 ✓

7. 6:00 ✓

8. 9:00 ✓

Problems 9-12: Draw hands on each clock so they represent the corresponding times.

9. 6:00

10. 11:00

11. 12:00

12. 3:00

Name: _____

Problems 1-4: Shade the circle with the correct answer.

1.
Ⓐ 12:00
Ⓑ 10:00
Ⓒ 2:00
Ⓓ 7:00

2.
Ⓐ 3:00
Ⓑ 4:00
Ⓒ 1:00
Ⓓ 8:00

3.
Ⓐ 1:00
Ⓑ 11:00
Ⓒ 5:00
Ⓓ 6:00

4.
Ⓐ 1:00
Ⓑ 2:00
Ⓒ 3:00
Ⓓ 10:00

Problems 5-8: Write the correct time on the line beneath each clock.

5. _____

6. _____

7. _____

8. _____

Problems 9-12: Draw hands on each clock so they represent the corresponding times.

9. __8:00__

10. __11:00__

11. __6:00__

12. __10:00__

Name: _____

Score:

Problems 1-4: Shade the circle with the correct answer.

1. Ⓐ 5:00
    Ⓑ 1:00
    Ⓒ 9:00
    Ⓓ 3:00

2. Ⓐ 2:00
    Ⓑ 12:00
    Ⓒ 4:00
    Ⓓ 1:00

3. Ⓐ 5:00
    Ⓑ 6:00
    Ⓒ 3:00
    Ⓓ 4:00

4. Ⓐ 2:00
    Ⓑ 8:00
    Ⓒ 7:00
    Ⓓ 10:00

Problems 5-8: Write the correct time on the line beneath each clock.

5. _____

6. _____

7. _____

8. _____

Problems 9-12: Draw hands on each clock so they represent the corresponding times.

9. ___2:00___

10. ___6:00___

11. ___10:00___

12. ___3:00___

Name: _____

Score:

Problems 1-4: Shade the circle with the correct answer.

1. Ⓐ 12:45
   Ⓑ 1:30
   Ⓒ 1:15
   Ⓓ (12:30)

2. Ⓐ (3:45)
   Ⓑ 3:15
   Ⓒ 9:15
   Ⓓ (2:45)

3. Ⓐ 7:15
   Ⓑ 4:15
   Ⓒ 3:15
   Ⓓ (6:15)

4. Ⓐ (7:00)
   Ⓑ 6:00
   Ⓒ 12:00
   Ⓓ 5:00

Problems 5-8: Write the correct time on the line beneath each clock.

5. _3:30_

6. _8:15_

7. _11:45_

8. _12:15_

Problems 9-12: Draw hands on each clock so they represent the corresponding times.

9. _5:00_

10. _3:45_

11. _9:30_

12. _10:15_

Name: _____

Problems 1-4: Shade the circle with the correct answer.

1. Ⓐ 3:45
    Ⓑ 5:45
    Ⓒ 4:45
    Ⓓ 9:45

2. Ⓐ 12:45
    Ⓑ 9:45
    Ⓒ 11:45
    Ⓓ 10:45

3. Ⓐ 7:30
    Ⓑ 6:45
    Ⓒ 8:45
    Ⓓ 8:30

4. Ⓐ 6:30
    Ⓑ 6:15
    Ⓒ 3:30
    Ⓓ 7:15

Problems 5-8: Write the correct time on the line beneath each clock.

5. _____ 6. _____ 7. _____ 8. _____

Problems 9-12: Draw hands on each clock so they represent the corresponding times.

9. __5:30__ 10. __11:15__ 11. __1:45__ 12. __3:45__

Name: _____

Score:

Problems 1-4: Shade the circle with the correct answer.

1. Ⓐ 3:45
   Ⓑ 4:15
   Ⓒ 9:15
   Ⓓ 2:45

2. Ⓐ 4:45
   Ⓑ 9:30
   Ⓒ 11:45
   Ⓓ 10:45

3. Ⓐ 3:15
   Ⓑ 2:15
   Ⓒ 1:15
   Ⓓ 12:15

4. Ⓐ 4:30
   Ⓑ 6:15
   Ⓒ 6:30
   Ⓓ 5:30

Problems 5-8: Write the correct time on the line beneath each clock.

5. _____

6. _____

7. _____

8. _____

Problems 9-12: Draw hands on each clock so they represent the corresponding times.

9. __6:00__

10. __8:15__

11. __11:45__

12. __2:30__

Name: _____

Score:

Problems 1-4: Shade the circle with the correct answer.

1. Ⓐ 11:15
    Ⓑ 12:15
    Ⓒ 3:00
    Ⓓ 1:15

2. Ⓐ 7:30
    Ⓑ 6:45
    Ⓒ 6:30
    Ⓓ 8:45

3. Ⓐ 9:30
    Ⓑ 6:45
    Ⓒ 6:30
    Ⓓ 5:45

4. Ⓐ 2:30
    Ⓑ 1:15
    Ⓒ 3:15
    Ⓓ 2:15

Problems 5-8: Write the correct time on the line beneath each clock.

5. _____

6. _____

7. _____

8. _____

Problems 9-12: Draw hands on each clock so they represent the corresponding times.

9. __12:15__

10. __4:30__

11. __9:45__

12. __7:00__

© Libro Studio LLC 2020

Name: _____

Score:

Problems 1-4: Shade the circle with the correct answer.

1. Ⓐ 6:45
    Ⓑ 9:30
    Ⓒ 8:45
    Ⓓ 5:45

2. Ⓐ 2:15
    Ⓑ 2:45
    Ⓒ 2:30
    Ⓓ 3:15

3. Ⓐ 6:45
    Ⓑ 12:30
    Ⓒ 11:30
    Ⓓ 6:00

4. Ⓐ 8:15
    Ⓑ 3:45
    Ⓒ 8:30
    Ⓓ 9:15

Problems 5-8: Write the correct time on the line beneath each clock.

5. _____ 6. _____ 7. _____ 8. _____

Problems 9-12: Draw hands on each clock so they represent the corresponding times.

9. __1:30__   10. __4:00__   11. __9:15__   12. __12:45__

Name: _____

Score:

Problems 1-4: Shade the circle with the correct answer.

1. Ⓐ 6:45
    Ⓑ 9:30
    Ⓒ 9:00
    Ⓓ 5:45

2. Ⓐ 4:30
    Ⓑ 5:45
    Ⓒ 4:45
    Ⓓ 9:30

3. Ⓐ 11:15
    Ⓑ 12:30
    Ⓒ 12:15
    Ⓓ 3:00

4. Ⓐ 3:30
    Ⓑ 5:15
    Ⓒ 5:30
    Ⓓ 3:15

Problems 5-8: Write the correct time on the line beneath each clock.

5. _____

6. _____

7. _____

8. _____

Problems 9-12: Draw hands on each clock so they represent the corresponding times.

9. ___7:15___

10. ___2:30___

11. ___12:45___

12. ___10:15___

Name: _____

Score:

Problems 1-4: Shade the circle with the correct answer.

1. Ⓐ 10:45
   Ⓑ 11:45
   Ⓒ 9:45
   Ⓓ 12:45

2. Ⓐ 6:15
   Ⓑ 1:30
   Ⓒ 5:15
   Ⓓ 12:30

3. Ⓐ 12:30
   Ⓑ 6:00
   Ⓒ 12:15
   Ⓓ 12:00

4. Ⓐ 11:45
   Ⓑ 12:45
   Ⓒ 9:00
   Ⓓ 9:45

Problems 5-8: Write the correct time on the line beneath each clock.

5. _____

6. _____

7. _____

8. _____

Problems 9-12: Draw hands on each clock so they represent the corresponding times.

9. __8:15__

10. __4:30__

11. __7:15__

12. __3:45__

Name: _____

Problems 1-4: Shade the circle with the correct answer.

1. Ⓐ 5:30
    Ⓑ 9:30
    Ⓒ 6:30
    Ⓓ 5:45

2. Ⓐ 7:00
    Ⓑ 12:30
    Ⓒ 8:00
    Ⓓ 6:00

3. Ⓐ 12:15
    Ⓑ 1:15
    Ⓒ 12:15
    Ⓓ 3:15

4. Ⓐ 8:30
    Ⓑ 6:45
    Ⓒ 9:30
    Ⓓ 9:45

Problems 5-8: Write the correct time on the line beneath each clock.

5. _____   6. _____   7. _____   8. _____

Problems 9-12: Draw hands on each clock so they represent the corresponding times.

9. __3:45__   10. __11:15__   11. __9:30__   12. __5:15__

Day 69

Five Minutes

Name: _____

Problems 1-4: Shade the circle with the correct answer.

  (clock 3)

1. Ⓐ 4:50
    Ⓑ 10:25
    Ⓒ 5:50
    Ⓓ 5:45

2. Ⓐ 12:20
    Ⓑ 12:25
    Ⓒ 1:25
    Ⓓ 1:30

3. Ⓐ 2:40
    Ⓑ 2:35
    Ⓒ 3:40
    Ⓓ 3:45

4. Ⓐ 11:10
    Ⓑ 11:05
    Ⓒ 11:00
    Ⓓ 10:05

Problems 5-8: Write the correct time on the line beneath each clock.

5. _____

6. _____

7. _____

8. _____

Problems 9-12: Draw hands on each clock so they represent the corresponding times.

9. **9:20**

10. **1:35**

11. **12:50**

12. **6:40**

Name: _____

Problems 1-4: Shade the circle with the correct answer.

1. Ⓐ 2:50
   Ⓑ 10:20
   Ⓒ 10:10
   Ⓓ 2:45

2. Ⓐ 12:30
   Ⓑ 6:05
   Ⓒ 1:30
   Ⓓ 1:15

3. Ⓐ 7:40
   Ⓑ 6:40
   Ⓒ 8:40
   Ⓓ 8:35

4. Ⓐ 2:25
   Ⓑ 3:25
   Ⓒ 4:15
   Ⓓ 5:15

Problems 5-8: Write the correct time on the line beneath each clock.

5. _____

6. _____

7. _____

8. _____

Problems 9-12: Draw hands on each clock so they represent the corresponding times.

9. __11:50__

10. __4:10__

11. __7:45__

12. __2:35__

Day 71

Five Minutes

Name: _____

Problems 1-4: Shade the circle with the correct answer.

1.　Ⓐ 8:20
　　Ⓑ 8:05
　　Ⓒ 8:25
　　Ⓓ 8:10

2.　Ⓐ 1:30
　　Ⓑ 1:25
　　Ⓒ 2:25
　　Ⓓ 2:30

3.　Ⓐ 6:45
　　Ⓑ 6:35
　　Ⓒ 7:40
　　Ⓓ 7:45

4.　Ⓐ 4:10
　　Ⓑ 5:50
　　Ⓒ 4:50
　　Ⓓ 5:10

Problems 5-8: Write the correct time on the line beneath each clock.

5. _____

6. _____

7. _____

8. _____

Problems 9-12: Draw hands on each clock so they represent the corresponding times.

9. __1:10__

10. __8:20__

11. __9:05__

12. __4:50__

Problems 1-4: Shade the circle with the correct answer.

1. Ⓐ 2:55
    Ⓑ 11:15
    Ⓒ 11:30
    Ⓓ 3:55

2. Ⓐ 6:50
    Ⓑ 5:30
    Ⓒ 5:35
    Ⓓ 6:25

3. Ⓐ 3:40
    Ⓑ 8:15
    Ⓒ 4:40
    Ⓓ 8:20

4. Ⓐ 1:30
    Ⓑ 5:30
    Ⓒ 6:05
    Ⓓ 6:10

Problems 5-8: Write the correct time on the line beneath each clock.

5. _____

6. _____

7. _____

8. _____

Problems 9-12: Draw hands on each clock so they represent the corresponding times.

9. __6:30__

10. __11:15__

11. __2:35__

12. __7:55__

Name: _____

Problems 1-4: Shade the circle with the correct answer.

1. Ⓐ 6:40
    Ⓑ 6:30
    Ⓒ 6:35
    Ⓓ 7:35

2. Ⓐ 9:50
    Ⓑ 9:55
    Ⓒ 11:45
    Ⓓ 8:55

3. Ⓐ 5:45
    Ⓑ 5:30
    Ⓒ 6:45
    Ⓓ 9:30

4. Ⓐ 10:50
    Ⓑ 5:10
    Ⓒ 10:25
    Ⓓ 5:10

Problems 5-8: Write the correct time on the line beneath each clock.

5. _____ 6. _____ 7. _____ 8. _____

Problems 9-12: Draw hands on each clock so they represent the corresponding times.

9. __12:30__   10. __8:55__   11. __5:25__   12. __1:05__

Name: _____

Problems 1-4: Shade the circle with the correct answer.

   (clock 4)

1. Ⓐ 9:15
    Ⓑ 9:30
    Ⓒ 3:45
    Ⓓ 10:15

2. Ⓐ 11:00
    Ⓑ 2:20
    Ⓒ 2:10
    Ⓓ 2:00

3. Ⓐ 10:25
    Ⓑ 9:25
    Ⓒ 9:50
    Ⓓ 10:50

4. Ⓐ 11:05
    Ⓑ 1:55
    Ⓒ 11:10
    Ⓓ 12:55

Problems 5-8: Write the correct time on the line beneath each clock.

5. _____   6. _____   7. _____   8. _____

Problems 9-12: Draw hands on each clock so they represent the corresponding times.

9. __4:45__   10. __2:15__   11. __10:40__   12. __8:50__

Name: _____

Score:

Problems 1-4: Shade the circle with the correct answer.

1. Ⓐ 6:35
    Ⓑ 7:30
    Ⓒ 5:35
    Ⓓ 12:50

2. Ⓐ 8:10
    Ⓑ 2:40
    Ⓒ 3:40
    Ⓓ 8:30

3. Ⓐ 2:15
    Ⓑ 1:55
    Ⓒ 2:55
    Ⓓ 11:10

4. Ⓐ 10:20
    Ⓑ 10:15
    Ⓒ 4:50
    Ⓓ 4:15

Problems 5-8: Write the correct time on the line beneath each clock.

5. _____

6. _____

7. _____

8. _____

Problems 9-12: Draw hands on each clock so they represent the corresponding times.

9. **5:45**

10. **2:40**

11. **3:25**

12. **11:20**

Name: _____

Problems 1-4: Shade the circle with the correct answer.

1. Ⓐ 7:20
   Ⓑ 7:30
   Ⓒ 4:07
   Ⓓ 4:20

2. Ⓐ 8:20
   Ⓑ 8:25
   Ⓒ 8:10
   Ⓓ 8:30

3. Ⓐ 11:25
   Ⓑ 12:30
   Ⓒ 12:25
   Ⓓ 11:35

4. Ⓐ 6:40
   Ⓑ 5:25
   Ⓒ 6:25
   Ⓓ 5:50

Problems 5-8: Write the correct time on the line beneath each clock.

5. _____   6. _____   7. _____   8. _____

Problems 9-12: Draw hands on each clock so they represent the corresponding times.

9. ___4:55___   10. ___3:40___   11. ___11:15___   12. ___12:00___

Name: _____

Problems 1-4: Shade the circle with the correct answer.

1.	2.	3.	4.
Ⓐ 1:12	Ⓐ 12:24	Ⓐ 6:06	Ⓐ 7:10
Ⓑ 1:02	Ⓑ 12:20	Ⓑ 6:05	Ⓑ 7:08
Ⓒ 1:05	Ⓒ 12:05	Ⓒ 6:07	Ⓒ 7:07
Ⓓ 12:02	Ⓓ 12:04	Ⓓ 6:10	Ⓓ 7:05

Problems 5-8: Write the correct time on the line beneath each clock.

5. _____ 6. _____ 7. _____ 8. _____

Problems 9-12: Draw hands on each clock so they represent the corresponding times.

9. **12:32**   10. **12:47**   11. **11:18**   12. **1:18**

Name: _____

Score:

Problems 1-4: Shade the circle with the correct answer.

1. Ⓐ 10:30
    Ⓑ 10:32
    Ⓒ 10:33
    Ⓓ 7:50

2. Ⓐ 8:39
    Ⓑ 7:39
    Ⓒ 7:38
    Ⓓ 8:38

3. Ⓐ 5:25
    Ⓑ 5:43
    Ⓒ 5:44
    Ⓓ 5:35

4. Ⓐ 9:48
    Ⓑ 9:45
    Ⓒ 8:46
    Ⓓ 9:50

Problems 5-8: Write the correct time on the line beneath each clock.

5. _____   6. _____   7. _____   8. _____

Problems 9-12: Draw hands on each clock so they represent the corresponding times.

9. ___7:18___   10. ___7:26___   11. ___7:38___   12. ___7:46___

Day 79

Minutes

Name: _____

Problems 1-4: Shade the circle with the correct answer.

1. Ⓐ 10:15
    Ⓑ 10:14
    Ⓒ 10:13
    Ⓓ 10:12

2. Ⓐ 7:20
    Ⓑ 7:21
    Ⓒ 7:22
    Ⓓ 7:23

3. Ⓐ 7:25
    Ⓑ 7:30
    Ⓒ 7:39
    Ⓓ 7:38

4. Ⓐ 6:47
    Ⓑ 6:45
    Ⓒ 6:46
    Ⓓ 6:28

Problems 5-8: Write the correct time on the line beneath each clock.

5. _____   6. _____   7. _____   8. _____

Problems 9-12: Draw hands on each clock so they represent the corresponding times.

9. ___2:36___   10. ___9:17___   11. ___7:13___   12. ___4:17___

Name: _____

Problems 1-4: Shade the circle with the correct answer.

1. Ⓐ 8:02
   Ⓑ 8:01
   Ⓒ 8:03
   Ⓓ 8:10

2. Ⓐ 10:02
   Ⓑ 10:03
   Ⓒ 10:04
   Ⓓ 10:05

3. Ⓐ 5:02
   Ⓑ 5:03
   Ⓒ 6:06
   Ⓓ 5:06

4. Ⓐ 6:04
   Ⓑ 6:09
   Ⓒ 6:10
   Ⓓ 6:02

Problems 5-8: Write the correct time on the line beneath each clock.

5. _____

6. _____

7. _____

8. _____

Problems 9-12: Draw hands on each clock so they represent the corresponding times.

9. ___2:16___

10. ___4:18___

11. ___11:12___

12. ___10:48___

Name: _____

Score:

Problems 1-4: Shade the circle with the correct answer.

1. Ⓐ 6:20
    Ⓑ 6:21
    Ⓒ 6:22
    Ⓓ 6:23

2. Ⓐ 7:27
    Ⓑ 7:20
    Ⓒ 7:28
    Ⓓ 7:25

3. Ⓐ 9:25
    Ⓑ 9:32
    Ⓒ 6:45
    Ⓓ 6:46

4. Ⓐ 11:40
    Ⓑ 11:45
    Ⓒ 11:34
    Ⓓ 11:33

Problems 5-8: Write the correct time on the line beneath each clock.

5. _____   6. _____   7. _____   8. _____

Problems 9-12: Draw hands on each clock so they represent the corresponding times.

9. __11:08__   10. __6:24__   11. __7:18__   12. __8:19__

Name: _____

Problems 1-4: Shade the circle with the correct answer.

1.
Ⓐ 12:24
Ⓑ 12:25
Ⓒ 11:24
Ⓓ 11:23

2.
Ⓐ 5:28
Ⓑ 5:29
Ⓒ 5:26
Ⓓ 6:30

3.
Ⓐ 9:25
Ⓑ 9:32
Ⓒ 9:50
Ⓓ 9:12

4.
Ⓐ 2:37
Ⓑ 3:46
Ⓒ 2:35
Ⓓ 2:36

Problems 5-8: Write the correct time on the line beneath each clock.

5. _____

6. _____

7. _____

8. _____

Problems 9-12: Draw hands on each clock so they represent the corresponding times.

9. ___1:18___

10. ___3:41___

11. ___4:57___

12. ___9:18___

Name: _____

Problems 1-4: Shade the circle with the correct answer.

1. Ⓐ 10:30
   Ⓑ 10:13
   Ⓒ 10:12
   Ⓓ 10:14

2. Ⓐ 5:17
   Ⓑ 5:16
   Ⓒ 5:15
   Ⓓ 5:14

3. Ⓐ 3:25
   Ⓑ 3:30
   Ⓒ 3:22
   Ⓓ 3:35

4. Ⓐ 5:29
   Ⓑ 6:29
   Ⓒ 7:29
   Ⓓ 5:30

Problems 5-8: Write the correct time on the line beneath each clock.

5. _____   6. _____   7. _____   8. _____

Problems 9-12: Draw hands on each clock so they represent the corresponding times.

9. __2:28__   10. __12:17__   11. __7:43__   12. __8:13__

Day 84
Minutes

Name: _____

Problems 1-4: Shade the circle with the correct answer.

1. Ⓐ 5:24
    Ⓑ 5:21
    Ⓒ 5:18
    Ⓓ 5:27

2. Ⓐ 10:19
    Ⓑ 10:29
    Ⓒ 10:26
    Ⓓ 6:18

3. Ⓐ 10:25
    Ⓑ 10:30
    Ⓒ 10:50
    Ⓓ 10:37

4. Ⓐ 6:44
    Ⓑ 6:45
    Ⓒ 9:35
    Ⓓ 9:42

Problems 5-8: Write the correct time on the line beneath each clock.

5. _____

6. _____

7. _____

8. _____

Problems 9-12: Draw hands on each clock so they represent the corresponding times.

9. ___**6:19**___

10. ___**12:28**___

11. ___**7:02**___

12. ___**3:43**___

Name: _____

Problems 1-4: Shade the circle with the correct answer.

1.
Ⓐ 7:56
Ⓑ 7:55
Ⓒ 6:56
Ⓓ 6:58

2.
Ⓐ 12:52
Ⓑ 2:50
Ⓒ 12:10
Ⓓ 1:52

3.
Ⓐ 6:55
Ⓑ 6:54
Ⓒ 6:50
Ⓓ 7:54

4.
Ⓐ 7:10
Ⓑ 6:08
Ⓒ 7:08
Ⓓ 6:12

Problems 5-8: Write the correct time on the line beneath each clock.

5. _____

6. _____

7. _____

8. _____

Problems 9-12: Draw hands on each clock so they represent the corresponding times.

9. _____3:28_____

10. _____10:29_____

11. _____10:46_____

12. _____9:11_____

Name: _____

Problems 1-4: Shade the circle with the correct answer.

1.	Ⓐ 10:22	2.	Ⓐ 4:34	3.	Ⓐ 10:25	4.	Ⓐ 5:43
	Ⓑ 10:32		Ⓑ 4:33		Ⓑ 10:36		Ⓑ 5:45
	Ⓒ 10:35		Ⓒ 5:33		Ⓒ 10:37		Ⓒ 5:42
	Ⓓ 10:11		Ⓓ 5:44		Ⓓ 10:38		Ⓓ 5:51

Problems 5-8: Write the correct time on the line beneath each clock.

5. _____ 6. _____ 7. _____ 8. _____

Problems 9-12: Draw hands on each clock so they represent the corresponding times.

9. __12:09__ 10. __2:08__ 11. __5:19__ 12. __3:19__

Name: _____

Problems 1-4: Draw hands on each clock so they represent the corresponding times.

1. __Quarter to five__   2. __Ten after nine__   3. __Two fifteen__   4. __Four O-five__

Problems 5-8: Shade the circle with the correct answer.

5. Five to ten
   - Ⓐ 10:05
   - Ⓑ 10:55
   - Ⓒ 9:55
   - Ⓓ 5:10

6. Quarter after three
   - Ⓐ 3:45
   - Ⓑ 3:20
   - Ⓒ 3:30
   - Ⓓ 3:15

7. Eight forty-two
   - Ⓐ 8:42
   - Ⓑ 8:59
   - Ⓒ 8:40
   - Ⓓ 8:57

8. Four ten
   - Ⓐ 4:50
   - Ⓑ 4:05
   - Ⓒ 4:40
   - Ⓓ 4:10

Problems 9-12: Solve each word problem.

9. Jacobs flight left at 10:47 a.m. and landed at 2:15 p.m. How long was his flight?

10. Amanda's mom says she must go to bed at 9 pm. It is 7:40 p.m. now. How much time does she have before her bedtime?

11. Shannon played video games for 37 minutes. Ben played video games for 1 hour and 21 minutes. How much longer did Ben play than Shannon?

12. Pam left her house at 8:26 a.m. She went to the store, the bank, and got her hair cut. She did not get back home until 10:54 a.m. How long was she gone?

Name: _____

Problems 1-4: Draw hands on each clock so they represent the corresponding times.

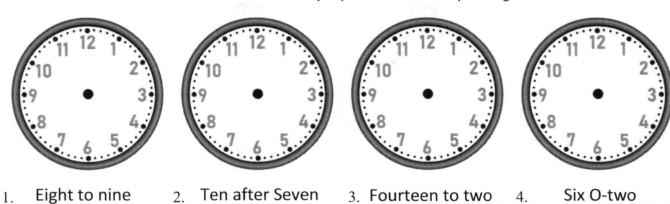

1. ___Eight to nine___ 2. ___Ten after Seven___ 3. ___Fourteen to two___ 4. ___Six O-two___

Problems 5-8: Shade the circle with the correct answer.

5. Twenty to five	6. Five to eleven	7. Four thirty	8. Nine fifty-four
Ⓐ 4:40	Ⓐ 10:52	Ⓐ 3:40	Ⓐ 9:04
Ⓑ 5:40	Ⓑ 11:05	Ⓑ 4:30	Ⓑ 8:40
Ⓒ 4:20	Ⓒ 10:55	Ⓒ 4:13	Ⓒ 9:40
Ⓓ 5:20	Ⓓ 10:05	Ⓓ 4:57	Ⓓ 9:54

Problems 9-12: Solve each word problem.

9. Kyle arrived at the amusement park at 9:45 a.m. He did not leave until 6:19 p.m. How much time did he spend at the park?

10. Kyle had to wait in line for his favorite rollercoaster ride. He got in line at 11:43 a.m. and had to wait for 25 minutes before entering the ride. What time was it when he entered the ride?

11. Alex is babysitting his neighbors' kids. He started watching them at 4:10 p.m., and their parents did not come back until 7:55 p.m. How long was he babysitting?

12. Bella went to a parade. It started at 2 p.m. and did not end until 3:16 p.m. How long did the parade last?

Name: _____

Score:

Problems 1-4: Draw hands on each clock so they represent the corresponding times.

1. __Eight thirty-nine__   2. __Twenty after two__   3. __Seven ten__   4. __Twelve to nine__

Problems 5-8: Shade the circle with the correct answer.

5. Three O-six
Ⓐ 6:03
Ⓑ 3:36
Ⓒ 3:06
Ⓓ 6:33

6. Ten twenty-one
Ⓐ 10:21
Ⓑ 1:20
Ⓒ 12:20
Ⓓ 1:10

7. Ten after five
Ⓐ 5:50
Ⓑ 10:05
Ⓒ 4:50
Ⓓ 5:10

8. Fifteen to four
Ⓐ 4:15
Ⓑ 4:35
Ⓒ 4:45
Ⓓ 3:45

Problems 9-12: Solve each word problem.

9. Megan went to a birthday party at 11:30 a.m. Her dad came to pick her up from the party 4 hours and 45 minutes later. What time did she leave the party?

10. It started to rain at 10:35 a.m. and did not stop for 16 hours. What time did the rain finally stop?

11. Terry took her medicine at 9:30 a.m. She is supposed to take another dose 8 hours later. What time should the next dose be taken?

12. The fireworks show starts at sunset. It is currently 6:14 p.m. Sunset is not until 8:36 p.m. How much longer until the fireworks show begins?

Problems 1-4: Draw hands on each clock so they represent the corresponding times.

1. __Seven fifteen__   2. __Nine forty-two__   3. __Ten past three__   4. __Twenty to six__

Problems 5-8: Shade the circle with the correct answer.

5. Thirteen to one   6. Ten after twelve   7. Eight eleven   8. Twenty-five to one

Ⓐ 1:13   Ⓐ 1:10   Ⓐ 8:11   Ⓐ 1:25

Ⓑ 1:47   Ⓑ 12:10   Ⓑ 8:49   Ⓑ 12:35

Ⓒ 12:13   Ⓒ 10:53   Ⓒ 11:08   Ⓒ 12:45

Ⓓ 12:47   Ⓓ 10:22   Ⓓ 11:52   Ⓓ 1:45

Problems 9-12: Solve each word problem.

9. Pam goes to the pool at 3:05 p.m. and swims until 4:40 p.m. How long did she swim?

10. Nate's GPS says it will take him 50 minutes to drive to his grandma's house. He runs into slow traffic, so it takes 1 hour and 15 minutes instead. How much time did the slow traffic add to his drive?

11. Gavin is baking. He is supposed to roast the food for 2 hours, but forgot to set the timer when he put the food in. He thinks its been in for 25 minutes. How much longer does the food need to bake?

12. It is 3:15 p.m. now. What time should the food be taken out of the oven? (*Refer to the information in question 11 and the answer you found*)

Name: _____

Score:

Problems 1-4: *Write the value of each group.*

① £_____

② £_____

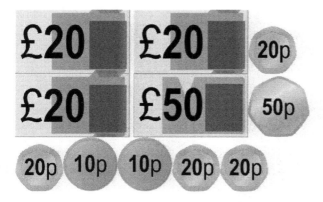

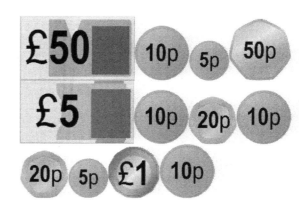

③ £_____

④ £_____

Problems 5-8: *Write the correct time on the line beneath each clock.*

⑤ _____

⑥ _____

⑦ _____

⑧ _____

Problems 9-11: *Add each set of fractions*

⑨ $5\frac{1}{6} + 1\frac{5}{6} =$

⑩ $2\frac{3}{4} + 3\frac{3}{4} =$

⑪ $1\frac{2}{7} + 4\frac{4}{7} =$

Name: _____

Score:

Problems 1-4: *Write the value of each group.*

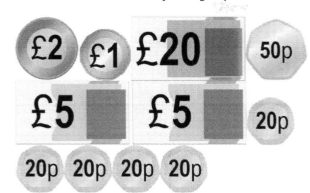

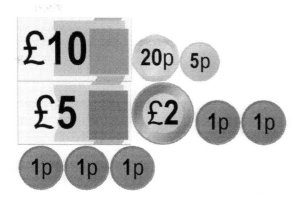

① £_____

② £_____

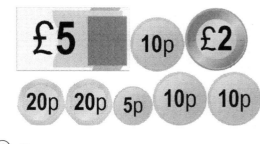

③ £_____

④ £_____

Problems 5-8: *Write the correct time on the line beneath each clock.*

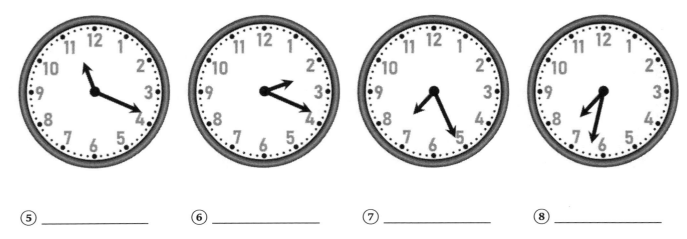

⑤ _____

⑥ _____

⑦ _____

⑧ _____

Problems 9-11: *Add each set of fractions*

⑨ $6\frac{1}{2} - 3 =$

⑩ $8\frac{1}{5} - 2\frac{3}{5} =$

⑪ $4\frac{5}{10} - 3\frac{3}{10} =$

Problems 1-4: *Write the value of each group.*

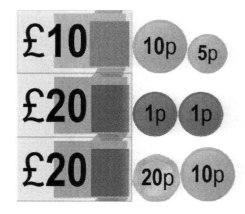

① £_____

② £_____

③ £_____

④ £_____

Problems 5-8: *Write the correct time on the line beneath each clock.*

⑤ _____

⑥ _____

⑦ _____

⑧ _____

Problems 9-11: *Add each set of fractions*

⑨ $2\frac{2}{4} + 5\frac{3}{4} =$

⑩ $4\frac{4}{7} + 3\frac{5}{7} =$

⑪ $1\frac{1}{3} + 1\frac{2}{3} =$

Name: _____

Score:

Problems 1-4: *Write the value of each group.*

① £_____

② £_____

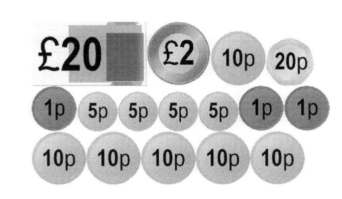

③ £_____

④ £_____

Problems 5-8: *Write the correct time on the line beneath each clock.*

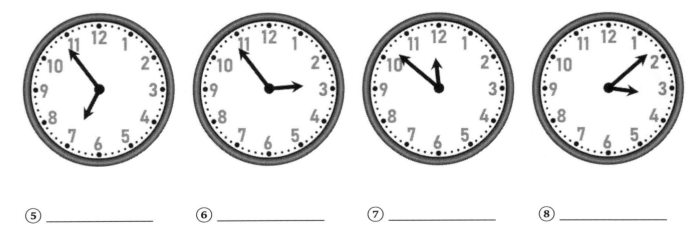

⑤ _____

⑥ _____

⑦ _____

⑧ _____

Problems 9-11: *Add each set of fractions*

⑨ $5\frac{4}{8} - 1\frac{5}{8} =$

⑩ $6\frac{1}{3} - 5\frac{2}{3} =$

⑪ $8\frac{9}{12} - 3\frac{8}{12} =$

Day 95
Mixed Review

Name: _____

Score:

Problems 1-4: *Write the value of each group.*

① £_____

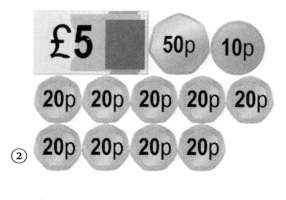

② £_____

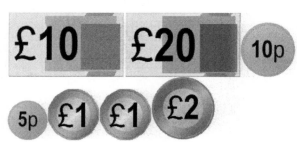

③ £_____

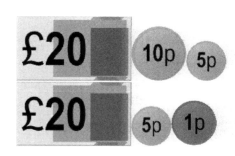

④ £_____

Problems 5-8: *Write the correct time on the line beneath each clock.*

⑤ _____   ⑥ _____   ⑦ _____   ⑧ _____

Problems 9-11: *Add each set of fractions*

⑨ $7\frac{1}{2} + \frac{1}{2} =$

⑩ $3\frac{3}{5} + 8\frac{3}{5} =$

⑪ $2\frac{5}{6} + 4\frac{3}{6} =$

Name: _____

Score:

Problems 1-4: Write the value of each group.

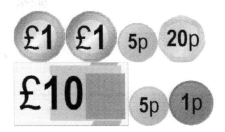

① £_____

② £_____

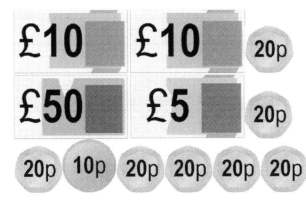

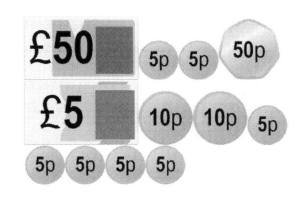

③ £_____

④ £_____

Problems 5-8: Write the correct time on the line beneath each clock.

⑤ _____
⑥ _____
⑦ _____
⑧ _____

Problems 9-11: Add each set of fractions

⑨ $7\frac{2}{4} - 5\frac{1}{4} =$

⑩ $9\frac{2}{6} - 1\frac{5}{6} =$

⑪ $5\frac{2}{7} - 2\frac{3}{7} =$

Name: _____

Score:

Problems 1-4: *Write the value of each group.*

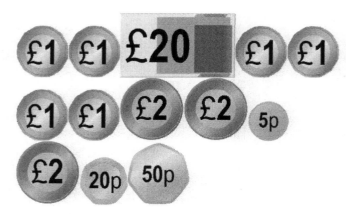

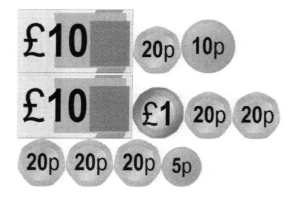

① £_____

② £_____

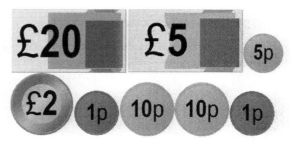

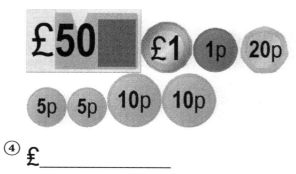

③ £_____

④ £_____

Problems 5-8: *Write the correct time on the line beneath each clock.*

⑤ _____ ⑥ _____ ⑦ _____ ⑧ _____

Problems 9-11: *Add each set of fractions*

⑨ $4\frac{4}{8} + 2\frac{6}{8} =$

⑩ $6\frac{1}{3} + 1\frac{1}{3} =$

⑪ $5\frac{7}{9} + 3\frac{6}{9} =$

Name: _____

Problems 1-4: *Write the value of each group.*

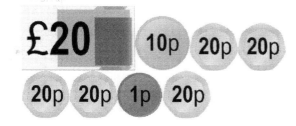

① £_____

② £_____

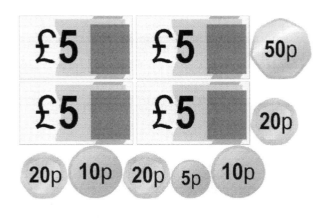

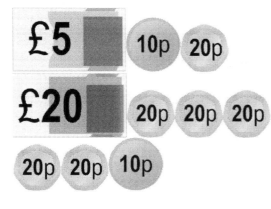

③ £_____

④ £_____

Problems 5-8: *Write the correct time on the line beneath each clock.*

⑤ _____

⑥ _____

⑦ _____

⑧ _____

Problems 9-11: *Add each set of fractions*

⑨ $4\frac{4}{5} - 4\frac{1}{5} =$

⑩ $9\frac{1}{4} - 5\frac{2}{4} =$

⑪ $8\frac{8}{10} - 1\frac{3}{10} =$

Name: _____

Score:

Problems 1-4: *Write the value of each group.*

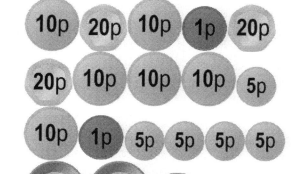

① £_____

② £_____

③ £_____

④ £_____

Problems 5-8: *Write the correct time on the line beneath each clock.*

⑤ _____

⑥ _____

⑦ _____

⑧ _____

Problems 9-11: *Add each set of fractions*

⑨ $5\frac{2}{5} + 2\frac{4}{5} =$

⑩ $1\frac{5}{9} + 1\frac{3}{9} =$

⑪ $3\frac{2}{4} + 6\frac{2}{4} =$

Name: _____

Score:

Problems 1-4: *Write the value of each group.*

① £_____

② £_____

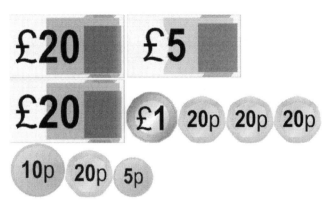

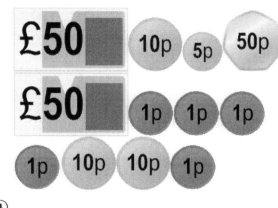

③ £_____

④ £_____

Problems 5-8: *Write the correct time on the line beneath each clock.*

⑤ _____

⑥ _____

⑦ _____

⑧ _____

Problems 9-11: *Add each set of fractions*

⑨ $6\frac{4}{7} - 5\frac{6}{7} =$

⑩ $3\frac{5}{9} - 1\frac{5}{9} =$

⑪ $7\frac{1}{6} - 3\frac{3}{6} =$

Answers

Day 1:
1) One penny 2) Two pence 3) Five pence
4) 1p 5) 2p 6) 5p
7) 7p 8) 20p 9) 7p 10) 14p
11) 20p 12) 36p 13) 58p 14) 51p 15) 92p
16) 59p 17) 15p 18) 83p 19) 71p 20) 90p

Day 2:
1) 8p 2) 10p 3) 19p 4) 13p
5) 23p 6) 15p 7) 37p 8) 31p
9) 32p 10) 31p 11) 50p 12) 19p

Day 3:
1) 10p 2) 13p 3) 33p 4) 20p
5) 60p 6) 25p 7) 43p 8) 29p

Day 4:
1) Ten pence 2) Twenty pence 3) Fifty
pence 4) 10p 5) 20p 6) 50p 7) 90p
8) 40p 9) 85p 10) 67p 11) 72p 12) 74p

Day 5:
1) 65p 2) 50p 3) 57p 4) 95p
5) 80p 6) 89p 7) 74p 8) 94p

Day 6:
1) 36p 2) 47p 3) 67p 4) 92p
5) 66p 6) 83p 7) 107p 8) 65p
9) 74p 10) 61p 11) 69p 12) 79p

Day 7:
1) 84p 2) 84p 3) 75p 4) 90p
5) 88p 6) 78p 7) 88p 8) 47p

Day 8:
1) 22p 2) 21p 3) 29p 4) 66p 5) 3p
6) 74p 7) 15p 8) 10p 9) 32p 10) 47p
11) 25p 12) 12p 13) 35p 14) 32p 15) 41p

Day 9:
1) 7p 2) 96p 3) 13p
4) 7 5) 44p 6) 64p

Day 10:
1) £0.20 2) £0.40 3) £0.60 4) £0.80
5) £1.00 6) £1.20 7) £1.40 8) £1.60
9) £1.80 10) £2.00 11) £2.60 12) £3.80
13) £5.00 14) £4.20

Day 11:
1) £1.87 2) £4.22 3) £8.91 4) £12.40
5) £8.95 6) £1.17 7) £1.25 8) £1.47
9) £1.45 10) £1.84 11) £2.50 12) £3.45
13) £2.09 14) £2.79 15) £2.97

Day 12:
1) 1 2) 2 3) 50 4) 10
5) 1 6) 4 7) 12 8) 50
9) 10 10) 8 11) 35 12) 10
13) 40 14) 8 15) 9 16) 12

Day 13:
1) £3.39 2) £7.54 3) £0.71 4) £8.06
5) £0.56 6) £7.00 7) £7.71 8) £4.31
9) £5.27 10) £7.75 11) £1.85 12) £1.81

Day 14:
1) £5.86 2) £1.01 3) £9.32
4) £6.87 5) £0.35 6) £2.08

Day 15:
1) One pound 2) Two pound 3) Five pound
4) Ten pound
5) £1.00 6) £2.00 7) £5.00 8) £10.00
9) £13.00 10) £21.00 11) £32.00 12)
£37.00

Day 16:
1) £9.00 2) £25.00 3) £22.00 4) £37.00
5) £77.00 6) £64.00 7) £45.00
8) £86.00 9) £81.00 10) £87.00

Day 17:
1) 1 2) 100 3) 3 4) 10 5) 20
6) 15 7) 500 8) 10 9) 5 10) 200

Day 18:
1) £5.59 2) £11.41 3) £16.45 4) £2.27
5) £16.20 6) £10.39 7) £28.40 8) £8.46

Day 19:
1) £53.55 2) £11.59 3) £38.12 4) £29.50
5) £53.65 6) £16.45 7) £33.80 8) £28.63
9) £34.33 10) £22.74 11) £41.71 12)
£27.45

Day 20:
1) £27.36 2) £24.85 3) £28.00
4) £18.00 5) £90.00 6) £27.15

Day 21:
1) Twenty-pound note 2) Fifty-pound note
3) £20.00 4) £50.00 5) £87.00
6) £140.00 7) £210.00
8) £123.00

Day 22:
1) £74.27 2) £52.90 3) £171.65
4) £43.15 5) £77.80 6) £157.85
7) £165.02 8) £246.86

Day 23:
1) 4 2) 5 3) 10 4) 20 5) 10
6) £74.32 7) £51.70 8) £62.32 9) £103.65

Day 24:
1) £84.98 2) £229.95 3) £76.47
4) £178.25 5) £74.50 6) £84.55
7) £410.00 8) £240.54 9) £326.00
10) £80.50 11) £80.75

Day 25:
1) £199.96 2) £249.00 3) £21.00
4) £180.00 5) £30.00 6) 16

Day 26:
1) 0, 1, 1, 4 2) 1, 1, 1, 3 3) 3, 0, 0, 1
4) 4, 1, 1, 2 5) 4, 0, 0, 3 6) 2, 1, 1, 1
7) 1, 0, 0, 4 8) 2, 0, 1, 0 9) 3, 1, 0, 2
10) 1, 1, 0, 3 11) 1, 0, 1, 1 12) 4, 1, 0, 0

Day 27:
1) 6, 0, 4, 1, 1, 0 2) 0, 1, 4, 3, 0, 1 3) 1, 1, 2, 4,
1, 0 4) 3, 0, 2, 1, 0, 0 5) 9, 1, 3, 2, 0, 0
6) 8, 0, 1, 2, 1, 1

Day 28:
1) 2, 0, 2, 2, 1, 1 2) 6, 0, 3, 0, 1, 1 3) 4, 1, 3, 4,
1, 0 4) 3, 1, 4, 3, 1, 0 5) 5, 0, 0, 2, 1, 0
6) 7, 1, 1, 4, 0, 1

Day 29:
1) $\frac{2}{3}$ 2) $\frac{1}{2}$ 3) $\frac{4}{5}$ 4) $\frac{2}{4}$ 5) $\frac{4}{5}$ 6) $\frac{5}{8}$
7) $\frac{3}{5}$ 8) $\frac{3}{4}$ 9) $\frac{7}{12}$ 10) $\frac{3}{4}$ 11) $\frac{1}{3}$ 12) $\frac{2}{3}$
13) $\frac{3}{6}$ 14) $\frac{7}{10}$ 15) $\frac{1}{2}$ 16) $\frac{2}{3}$ 17) $\frac{3}{4}$ 18) $\frac{1}{4}$

Day 30:
1) $\frac{5}{6}$ 2) $\frac{1}{4}$ 3) $\frac{2}{3}$ 4) $\frac{1}{2}$ 5) $\frac{5}{8}$ 6) $\frac{2}{4}$
7) $\frac{9}{16}$ 8) $\frac{3}{5}$ 9) $\frac{4}{6}$ 10) $\frac{2}{3}$ 11) $\frac{3}{5}$ 12) $\frac{1}{2}$
13) $\frac{3}{4}$ 14) $\frac{3}{8}$ 15) $\frac{3}{4}$ 16) $\frac{1}{3}$ 17) $\frac{2}{4}$ 18) $\frac{6}{8}$

Day 31:
1) $\frac{3}{5}$ 2) $\frac{2}{3}$ 3) $\frac{3}{8}$ 4) $\frac{5}{6}$ 5) $\frac{2}{10}$ 6) $\frac{2}{3}$
7) 1 8) 3 9) 6 10) 6

Day 32:
1) $\frac{4}{5}$ 2) $\frac{2}{3}$ 3) $\frac{2}{4}$ 4) $\frac{4}{6}$ 5) $\frac{1}{7}$ 6) $\frac{4}{6}$
7) $\frac{4}{8}$ 8) $\frac{6}{10}$ 9) $\frac{1}{4}$
*(Problems 10-18 are example answers.
Multiple ways of shading are possible.)*

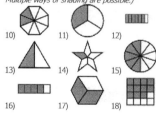

Day 33:
1) 5 2) 9 3) 5 4) 8 5) 6 6) 8 7) 15

Day 34:
1) $\frac{2}{4}$ 2) $\frac{4}{7}$ 3) $\frac{1}{5}$ 4) $\frac{3}{7}$
*(Problems 10-18 are example answers.
Multiple ways of shading are possible.)*

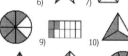

Day 35:
1) $\frac{3}{5}$ 2) $\frac{1}{3}$ 3) $\frac{6}{8}$ 4) $\frac{3}{4}$ 5) $\frac{1}{2}$ 6) $\frac{5}{6}$
7) $\frac{2}{3}$ 8) $\frac{7}{12}$ 9) $\frac{7}{10}$ 10) 2 11) 6 12) 3 13) 4

Day 36:
1) 6 2) 6 3) 15 4) 14 5) 9 6) 20 7) 2

Day 37:
1) < 2) = 3) > 4) > 5) < 6) >
7) = 8) < 9) = 10) > 11) < 12) =

Answers

Day 38:
1) 2 2) 3 3) 1 4) 2 5) 3
6) 1 7) 6 8) 1 9) 4 10) 3
11) 3 12) 3 13) 8 14) 2

Day 39:
1) = 2) > 3) < 4) <
5) > 6) = 7) > 8) >
9) < 10) = 11) > 12) <
13) = 14) >

Day 40:

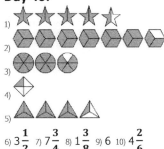

6) $3\frac{1}{2}$ 7) $7\frac{3}{4}$ 8) $1\frac{3}{8}$ 9) 6 10) $4\frac{2}{6}$

Day 41:
1) > 2) < 3) > 4) > 5) >
6) > 7) < 8) > 9) > 10) >
11) < 12) < 13) > 14) =

Day 42:
1) > 2) < 3) < 4) >
5) $\frac{7}{8}$, $1\frac{2}{3}$, $3\frac{1}{2}$, $3\frac{3}{5}$, $4\frac{1}{8}$, $6\frac{1}{3}$, $6\frac{3}{4}$
6) $3\frac{2}{5}$, $3\frac{5}{6}$, 4, $4\frac{1}{2}$, $4\frac{4}{5}$, $5\frac{1}{6}$, $5\frac{1}{3}$

Day 43:
1) $\frac{6}{8}$ 2) $\frac{3}{5}$ 3) $\frac{7}{10}$ 4) $\frac{4}{6}$ 5) $\frac{3}{4}$ 6) $\frac{2}{3}$
7) $\frac{2}{3}$ 8) $\frac{4}{5}$ 9) $\frac{9}{12}$ 10) $\frac{4}{6}$

Day 44:
1) $\frac{3}{6}$ 2) $\frac{4}{4}$ 3) $\frac{13}{16}$ 4) $\frac{5}{8}$ 5) $\frac{7}{9}$ 6) $\frac{4}{5}$ 7) $\frac{5}{6}$
8) $\frac{11}{15}$ 9) $\frac{3}{3}$ 10) $\frac{6}{5}$ 11) $\frac{11}{10}$ 12) $\frac{6}{7}$ 13) $\frac{3}{4}$
14) $\frac{5}{6}$ 15) $\frac{6}{9}$ 16) $\frac{5}{5}$ 17) $\frac{2}{11}$ 18) $\frac{4}{8}$ 19) $\frac{6}{7}$

Day 45:
1) $\frac{2}{5}$ 2) $\frac{1}{4}$ 3) $\frac{4}{8}$ 4) $\frac{1}{3}$ 5) $\frac{3}{10}$ 6) $\frac{2}{6}$
7) $\frac{2}{4}$ 8) $\frac{3}{8}$ 9) $\frac{3}{5}$ 10) $\frac{2}{6}$

Day 46:
1) $\frac{1}{6}$ 2) 0 3) $\frac{7}{16}$ 4) $\frac{3}{8}$ 5) $\frac{3}{6}$ 6) $\frac{4}{9}$ 7) $\frac{1}{5}$
8) $\frac{4}{10}$ 9) $\frac{9}{12}$ 10) $\frac{4}{8}$ 11) $\frac{1}{4}$ 12) $\frac{2}{7}$ 13) $\frac{1}{3}$
14) $\frac{11}{16}$ 15) $\frac{2}{10}$ 16) $\frac{1}{5}$ 17) $\frac{1}{6}$ 18) $\frac{3}{8}$ 19) $\frac{7}{9}$

Day 47:
1) $4\frac{6}{8}$ 2) $4\frac{3}{4}$ 3) $5\frac{3}{3}$ 4) $5\frac{1}{2}$ 5) $2\frac{5}{6}$
6) $4\frac{3}{4}$ 7) $3\frac{1}{2}$

Day 48:
1) $5\frac{1}{6}$ 2) $1\frac{1}{2}$ 3) $3\frac{4}{5}$ 4) 4
5) $8\frac{3}{4}$ 6) $6\frac{5}{6}$ 7) $8\frac{2}{3}$ 8) $5\frac{2}{7}$
9) $11\frac{4}{5}$ 10) $5\frac{10}{16}$ 11) $4\frac{2}{4}$ 12) $6\frac{5}{8}$
13) $12\frac{1}{2}$ 14) $5\frac{5}{7}$ 15) $5\frac{8}{9}$ 16) $6\frac{6}{10}$

Day 49:
1) $3\frac{2}{2}$ 2) $4\frac{8}{6}$ 3) $4\frac{4}{4}$ 4) $6\frac{2}{2}$ 5) $3\frac{4}{3}$
6) $2\frac{9}{6}$ 7) $3\frac{8}{8}$

Day 50:
1) $4\frac{3}{3}$ 2) $2\frac{6}{4}$ 3) $2\frac{6}{5}$ 4) $6\frac{13}{8}$
5) $7\frac{5}{4}$ 6) $6\frac{9}{7}$ 7) $1\frac{3}{3}$ 8) $4\frac{2}{2}$
9) $11\frac{10}{9}$ 10) $10\frac{19}{12}$ 11) $8\frac{7}{5}$ 12) $6\frac{8}{8}$
13) $11\frac{4}{3}$ 14) $12\frac{7}{6}$ 15) $2\frac{2}{2}$ 16) $9\frac{6}{4}$

Day 51:
1) $8\frac{6}{7}$ 2) $11\frac{3}{3}$ 3) $10\frac{2}{2}$ 4) $3\frac{6}{9}$ 5) $9\frac{5}{4}$ 6) $2\frac{6}{5}$
7) $8\frac{9}{8}$ 8) $5\frac{5}{8}$ 9) $16\frac{6}{10}$ 10) $7\frac{6}{7}$ 11) $9\frac{2}{2}$ 12) $7\frac{5}{3}$
13) $13\frac{6}{4}$ 14) $12\frac{7}{7}$ 15) $4\frac{6}{5}$ 16) $8\frac{2}{2}$ 17) $4\frac{3}{3}$ 18) $6\frac{10}{12}$
19) $6\frac{5}{7}$ 20) $9\frac{2}{2}$ 21) $10\frac{3}{3}$ 22) $3\frac{10}{9}$ 23) $8\frac{7}{5}$ 24) $9\frac{3}{4}$
25) $12\frac{10}{8}$ 26) $11\frac{6}{6}$ 27) $8\frac{2}{3}$

Day 52:
1) 1 2) $2\frac{1}{3}$ 3) $3\frac{2}{5}$ 4) $\frac{2}{4}$ 5) $2\frac{3}{8}$
6) 0 7) $1\frac{4}{10}$

Day 53:
1) 1 2) $1\frac{2}{4}$ 3) $2\frac{2}{6}$ 4) $\frac{2}{5}$
5) $3\frac{3}{7}$ 6) $6\frac{2}{4}$ 7) $1\frac{3}{8}$ 8) 4
9) $2\frac{2}{9}$ 10) 4 11) $6\frac{3}{8}$ 12) $2\frac{1}{5}$
13) $2\frac{4}{10}$ 14) 2 15) $2\frac{1}{7}$ 16) $6\frac{2}{6}$

Day 54:
1) $\frac{1}{2}$ 2) $1\frac{1}{2}$ 3) $1\frac{4}{5}$ 4) $1\frac{2}{3}$ 5) 3
6) $\frac{3}{4}$ 7) $\frac{7}{10}$

Day 55:
1) $1\frac{4}{5}$ 2) $\frac{1}{2}$ 3) $1\frac{2}{3}$ 4) $\frac{1}{3}$
5) $1\frac{5}{6}$ 6) $2\frac{3}{4}$ 7) $6\frac{1}{2}$ 8) $2\frac{3}{5}$
9) $\frac{5}{7}$ 10) $4\frac{1}{2}$ 11) $7\frac{2}{3}$ 12) $2\frac{1}{3}$
13) $1\frac{1}{3}$ 14) $4\frac{3}{4}$ 15) $\frac{1}{2}$ 16) $6\frac{3}{5}$

Day 56:
1) $5\frac{4}{5}$ 2) 4 3) $1\frac{5}{7}$ 4) $2\frac{1}{3}$ 5) $6\frac{4}{9}$ 6) $1\frac{5}{8}$
7) $\frac{1}{2}$ 8) $3\frac{1}{3}$ 9) $5\frac{3}{4}$ 10) $3\frac{5}{9}$ 11) $2\frac{2}{7}$ 12) $1\frac{4}{5}$
13) 2 14) $3\frac{1}{2}$ 15) $3\frac{1}{5}$ 16) 2 17) $4\frac{1}{4}$ 18) $4\frac{1}{3}$
19) $4\frac{2}{3}$ 20) $2\frac{2}{3}$ 21) $4\frac{3}{5}$ 22) 2 23) $8\frac{1}{7}$ 24) $6\frac{3}{7}$
25) $\frac{3}{5}$ 26) 2 27) $1\frac{1}{2}$

Day 57:
1) B 2) D 3) A 4) D
5) 8:00 6) 10:00 7) 3:00 8) 1:00

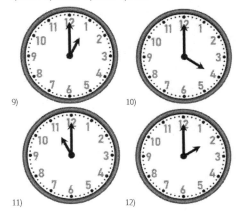

9) 10) 11) 12)

Day 58:
1) C 2) A 3) C 4) C
5) 12:00 6) 5:00 7) 6:00 8) 9:00

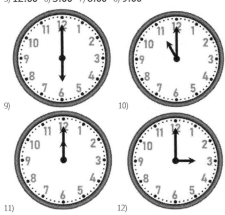

9) 10) 11) 12)

© Libro Studio LLC 2020

Day 59: 1) D 2) B 3) A 4) B
5) 5:00 6) 12:00 7) 9:00 8) 3:00

9)

11)

10)

12)

Day 63: 1) B 2) B 3) C 4) A
5) 8:45 6) 3:30 7) 6:15 8) 2:45

9)

11)

10)

12)

Day 67: 1) A 2) D 3) B 4) A
5) 8:00 6) 4:15 7) 1:45 8) 9:30

9)

11)

10)

12)

Day 60: 1) C 2) D 3) D 4) B
5) 1:00 6) 7:00 7) 2:00 8) 7:00

9)

11)

10)

12)

Day 64: 1) C 2) A 3) D 4) D
5) 4:15 6) 12:30 7) 9:30 8) 11:45

9)

11)

10)

12)

Day 68: 1) A 2) A 3) B 4) A
5) 3:15 6) 12:00 7) 10:00 8) 7:15

9)

11)

10)

12)

Day 61: 1) D 2) D 3) D 4) A
5) 3:30 6) 8:15 7) 11:45 8) 12:15

9)

11)

10)

12)

Day 65: 1) D 2) A 3) C 4) A
5) 1:45 6) 9:30 7) 10:00 8) 4:15

9)

11)

10)

12)

Day 69: 1) A 2) B 3) A 4) B
5) 10:45 6) 7:10 7) 6:50 8) 10:35

9)

11)

10)

12)

Day 62: 1) C 2) C 3) A 4) B
5) 4:15 6) 9:15 7) 10:00 8) 3:15

9)

11)

10)

12)

Day 66: 1) C 2) C 3) A 4) B
5) 8:00 6) 4:15 7) 1:45 8) 9:30

9)

11)

10)

12)

Day 70: 1) C 2) A 3) B 4) D
5) 4:25 6) 2:05 7) 7:55 8) 5:00

9)

11)

10)

12)

Day 71: 1) D 2) B 3) A 4) C
5) 12:05 6) 10:20 7) 2:30 8) 9:15

Day 75: 1) C 2) B 3) B 4) A
5) 6:15 6) 10:10 7) 11:05 8) 12:05

Day 79: 1) B 2) D 3) C 4) A
5) 9:53 6) 3:54 7) 7:29 8) 4:26

Day 72: 1) B 2) D 3) A 4) C
5) 5:25 6) 5:55 7) 1:30 8) 10:10

Day 76: 1) A 2) B 3) C 4) C
5) 9:25 6) 12:25 7) 6:30 8) 11:30

Day 80: 1) B 2) C 3) D 4) B
5) 1:13 6) 5:14 7) 8:17 8) 3:29

Day 73: 1) C 2) D 3) A 4) C
5) 12:45 6) 7:10 7) 9:40 8) 8:15

Day 77: 1) B 2) D 3) A 4) B
5) 5:43 6) 6:47 7) 7:37 8) 8:33

Day 81: 1) B 2) A 3) B 4) D
5) 8:26 6) 8:11 7) 12:03 8) 11:14

Day 74: 1) A 2) A 3) B 4) D
5) 6:10 6) 3:35 7) 4:20 8) 12:30

Day 78: 1) B 2) B 3) C 4) C
5) 8:09 6) 8:02 7) 5:47 8) 12:47

Day 82: 1) A 2) B 3) B 4) A
5) 1:44 6) 12:51 7) 3:29 8) 3:16

Day 83: 1) B 2) A 3) C 4) A
5) 3:28 6) 4:42 7) 12:59 8) 3:41

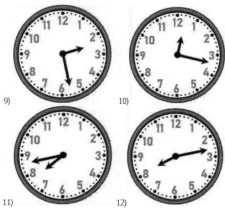

9)   10)

11)   12)

Day 84: 1) B 2) B 3) D 4) A
5) 12:44 6) 1:47 7) 8:59 8) 9:41

9)   10)

11)   12)

Day 85: 1) C 2) A 3) B 4) C
5) 11:09 6) 1:19 7) 11:23 8) 9:32

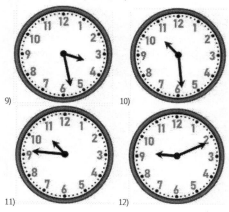

9)   10)

11)   12)

Day 86: 1) A 2) B 3) B 4) C
5) 6:46 6) 12:52 7) 1:57 8) 9:59

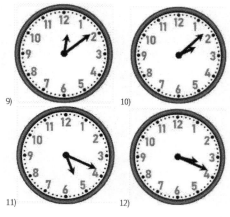

9)   10)

11)   12)

Day 87:

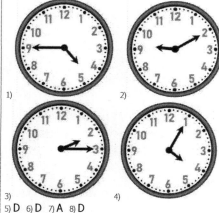

1)   2)

3)   4)

5) D 6) D 7) A 8) D
9) 3:28 10) 1:20 11) 0:44 12) 2:28

Day 88:

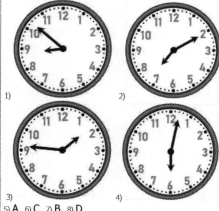

1)   2)

3)   4)

5) A 6) C 7) B 8) D
9) 8:34 10) 12:08 11) 3:45 12) 1:16

Day 89:

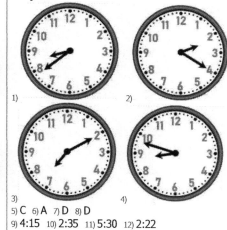

1)   2)

3)   4)

5) C 6) A 7) D 8) D
9) 4:15 10) 2:35 11) 5:30 12) 2:22

Day 90:

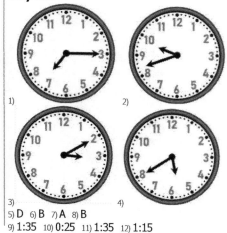

1)   2)

3)   4)

5) D 6) B 7) A 8) B
9) 1:35 10) 0:25 11) 1:35 12) 1:15

Day 91:
1) £25.97 2) £14.31 3) £111.50 4) £57.40
5) 7:19 6) 7:16 7) 12:11 8) 8:03
9) $6\frac{6}{6}$ 10) $5\frac{6}{4}$ 11) $5\frac{6}{7}$

Day 92:
1) £34.50 2) £17.30 3) £33.25 4) £7.75
5) 11:19 6) 2:19 7) 7:26 8) 7:32
9) $3\frac{1}{2}$ 10) $5\frac{3}{5}$ 11) $1\frac{2}{10}$

Day 93:
1) £26.22 2) £51.01 3) £116.00 4) £50.47
5) 6:17 6) 6:23 7) 12:23 8) 5:16
9) $7\frac{5}{4}$ 10) $7\frac{9}{7}$ 11) $2\frac{3}{3}$

Day 94:
1) £31.31 2) £70.65 3) £23.03 4) £43.34
5) 6:54 6) 2:54 7) 11:52 8) 3:08
9) $3\frac{7}{8}$ 10) $2\frac{2}{3}$ 11) $5\frac{1}{12}$

Day 95:
1) £200.00 2) £7.40 3) £34.15 4) £40.21
5) 8:49 6) 3:23 7) 1:21 8) 12:12
9) $7\frac{2}{2}$ 10) $11\frac{6}{5}$ 11) $6\frac{8}{6}$

Day 96:
1) £27.40 2) £12.31 3) £76.50 4) £56.05
5) 5:19 6) 2:08 7) 8:19 8) 6:22
9) $2\frac{1}{4}$ 10) $7\frac{1}{2}$ 11) $2\frac{6}{7}$

Day 97:
1) £32.75 2) £22.35 3) £27.27 4) £51.51
5) 6:26 6) 1:26 7) 12:26 8) 3:26
9) $6\frac{10}{8}$ 10) $7\frac{2}{3}$ 11) $8\frac{13}{9}$

Day 98:
1) £25.33 2) £21.11 3) £21.35 4) £26.40
5) 8:59 6) 12:57 7) 8:46 8) 7:21
9) $\frac{3}{5}$ 10) $3\frac{3}{4}$ 11) $7\frac{5}{10}$

Day 99:
1) £120.00 2) £6.47 3) 61p 4) £20.10
5) 5:47 6) 2:52 7) 3:56 8) 5:58
9) $7\frac{6}{5}$ 10) $2\frac{8}{9}$ 11) $9\frac{4}{4}$

Day 100:
1) £62.60 2) £5.70 3) £46.95 4) £100.90
5) 11:08 6) 12:08 7) 6:23 8) 9:32
9) $\frac{5}{7}$ 10) 2 11) $3\frac{2}{3}$

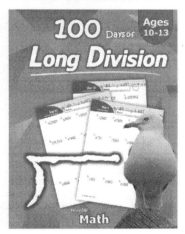

To view more Humble Math books, please visit www.HumbleMath.com.

ISBN: 978-1-63578-327-8   (GBP Edition)

Current contact information for Libro Studio LLC can be found at www.LibroStudioLLC.com

Printed in Poland
by Amazon Fulfillment
Poland Sp. z o.o., Wrocław

62531932R00060